My Guy 1985!

What's In Store!

Hi, everyone. You know, Julie may be rabbiting on about what a wonderful year she's had, but as far as I'm concerned, the past twelve months have been a total wash-out. Women trouble, I'm afraid.

It all started with this girl. I'll call her Cheryl (actually, I *did* call her Cheryl. To her face. Which is where the trouble started). I had high hopes about Cheryl. Unfortunately, she had high hopes about me, too — but they weren't quite the same as mine.

I first began to suspect trouble when she tried to measure me up for a morning suit. I mean to say, my idea of a morning suit is my pyjamas, right? But Cheryl thought differently.

And I knew something was definitely wrong when she started whistling *The Wedding March* every time there was a gap in the conversation. Subtle, huh?

Anyway, I decided to break it off there and then. No sense in hanging about, is there?

Of course, I know it'll take me a while to get over it. I'm very sensitive when it comes to women. But as I was saying to Michelle (or was it Candice?) only last night — I'm just not the marrying kind . . .

44 BE YOUR OWN MAKE-UP ARTIST
We show you the tricks of the trade — to make you look good!

60 I WAS DESPERATE FOR A FELLA!
A reader tells her heart-rending story

80 POP SPECIAL
The shy boy of Spandau

52 LOOKING GOOD, SPENDING LESS!
Looking great on a budget

78 COULD YOU BE A MODEL?
It's tough at the top — find out if you've got what it takes to make it in the hard world of fashion. You could be surprised!

PLUS

LOADS OF FEATURES, QUIZZES AND PIN-UPS!

It's all there. So what are you waiting for? Get on with it — and have lots of fun!

SBN 85037 655 6

£2.95

MY GUY JOB SPOT

Leaving school — or just looking for the job that you really want? Well, look no further — our Astro guide will tell you what you're ideally suited to . . . and why!

STAR SIGN	YOUR STRENGTHS	YOUR WEAKNESSES	YOUR IDEAL CAREERS	THE YEAR AHEAD
ARIES (MAR 21– APR 20)	You're a brilliant organiser and good at working on projects alone.	*You tend to be bossy and a bit too loud. You hate routine.*	Sales work. Journalism. Jobs that involve travel.	1985 will get off to a slow start career wise, but April will see an improvement.
TAURUS (APR 21– MAY 22)	You have an artistic nature and lots of taste. You enjoy creative work.	*You try too hard to succeed and don't take good advice when offered.*	Window dressing. Anything to do with fashion or advertising.	Success will only come if you work hard. June should see you settled.
GEMINI (MAY 23– JUNE 21)	You're great at getting people to agree with you and aim to please.	*You like to be praised all the time — and are an insecure person.*	Sales work. Catering or hotel management. Advertising.	This year will be a let down, but don't despair, big things start to happen in '86.
CANCER (JUNE 22– JULY 22)	You get on well with everyone you work with and make friends easily.	*You work far too hard and expect too much from yourself.*	Nursing. Looking after kids. Teaching. Social work.	A great year where you will achieve everything you want. You deserve it.
LEO (JULY 23– AUG 22)	You're artistic, ambitious and fun to work with. You have good ideas.	*You can try too hard to impress. You like things to go your way.*	Dress designing. Acting or dancing. Working in a florists.	A lucky break in November will set you on the road to fame and fortune.
VIRGO (AUG 23– SEP 22)	You have lots of energy and take a pride in working hard.	*You worry too much about minor details and lack confidence.*	Secretarial work. Book-keeping. Nursing.	You will impress someone very important who can help your career.
LIBRA (SEP 23– OCT 22)	You're creative and bursting with ideas. You also have a sense of humour.	*You like to work as part of a team and can be shy and lack confidence.*	Hairdressing. Dress designing. Receptionists. work.	Don't give up just because things go wrong in May. They *will* get better.
SCORPIO (OCT 23– NOV 21)	You're single minded and like a challenge. You're also very efficient.	*You can get yourself into hot water by thinking you know it all.*	Sales work. Social work. Administration or political work.	A year to plan ahead and work hard for what you want. But watch out for rivals.
SAGITTAR- IUS (NOV 22– DEC 22)	You're always on the go and cheerful. You'll happily work long hours.	*You talk too much and disturb others and like to get your own way.*	Outdoor work. Working with animals or children.	You may change jobs and find you've made a mistake. Start looking around again.
CAPRICORN (DEC 23– JAN 20)	You're a cool customer and work well under pressure. You never panic.	*You can give a 'couldn't care less' impression which is misleading.*	Administrative work. Banking. Tourism.	March will be a turning point — and one for the better. You've been very patient.
AQUARIUS (JAN 21– FEB 19)	You want the best for yourself and don't mind working hard for it.	*You expect quick results and tend to be impatient and aggressive.*	Public Relations. Working with the public in any capacity.	Don't rush into a job you're offered in May. It may not be the right one for you.
PISCES (FEB 20– MAR 20)	You're adaptable and try hard to make the most of your talents.	*You tend to step on others' toes to get what you want.*	Modelling or demonstrating work. Any job with no set routine.	You'll get nowhere fast this year, but you will enjoy yourself all the same.

Or if you want to be really romantic...

VIVE L'AMOUR!

"My mum's told me all about Gallic charm!"

Then fate took a hand. . .

Mind you, it wasn't too easy to get myself noticed. . .

HELLO, SHE'S LEFT SOME COINS ON THE TABLE — I CAN RUN AFTER HER AND GET THE TWO OF US TALKING.

ATTENTION! QU'EST—CE QUE VOUS FAITES?

I don't know what that meant, but I don't think it was too friendly — I reckoned he wanted the money for himself.

I MUST HAVE LOST HER IN THE CROWD BACK THERE. MAYBE SHE'LL GO BACK TO THAT CAFE WE WERE IN THIS MORNING.

EXCUSE ME, DO YOU SPEAK ENGLISH? I'M TRYING TO FIND NOTRE DAME CATHEDRAL.

OH. . .I GUESS YOU DON'T SPEAK ENGLISH. WELL, NEVER MIND — AU REVOIR!

I couldn't speak because I couldn't believe it! Life's like that — just when you think your luck's run out. . .

. . .it runs back in again!

WAIT! I—I DO SPEAK A LITTLE OF YOUR ENGLISH, MAM'SELLE — AND IF YOU ARE LIKING IT, I WILL SHOW YOU TO THE CATHEDRAL.

YOU'RE VERY KIND, BUT IT'S ALL RIGHT — I DON'T WANT TO PUT YOU TO ANY TROUBLE.

TROUBLE? TO SHOW PARIS TO A LOVELY GIRL SUCH AS YOUR-SELF, THIS IS NO TROUBLE. IT WAS YOUR BEAUTY THAT MADE ME LOSE MY VOICE BEFORE!

ALL RIGHT, THEN — YOU CAN SHOW ME AROUND. BUT LESS OF THE FLATTERY, OKAY? MY MUM'S TOLD ME ALL ABOUT GALLIC CHARM!

I didn't know what she was going on about — I hadn't touched a bit of garlic since I'd been there.

But we were together at last. . .

THIS ISN'T NOTRE DAME CATHEDRAL, IS IT?

ER, NO, NOT EXACTLY — BUT WE ARE VERY CLOSE TO IT, MAM'SELLE.

I had a bit of trouble showing her round Paris — I didn't know the place too well myself.

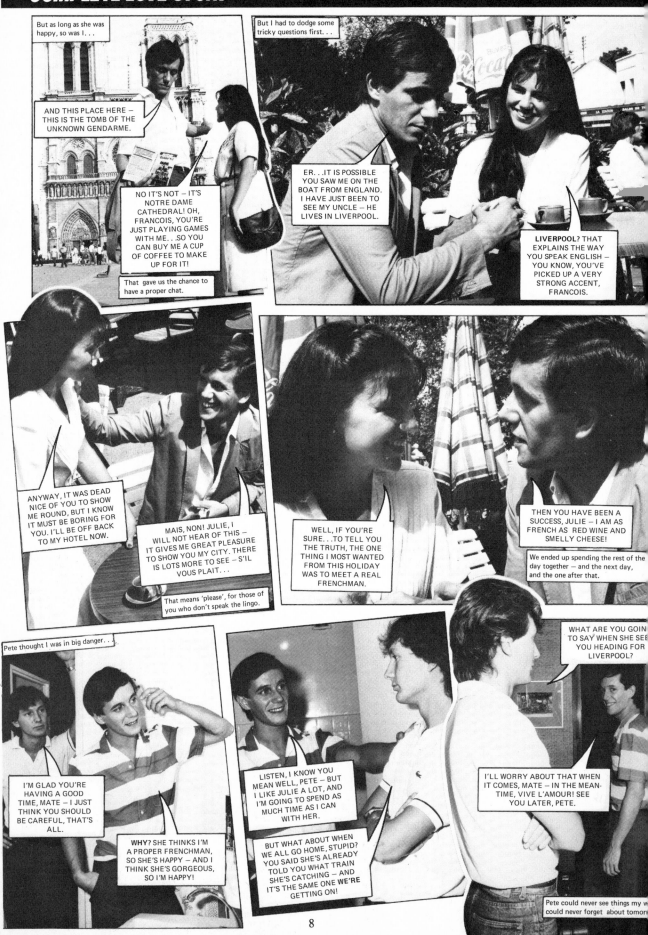

But as long as she was happy, so was I...

AND THIS PLACE HERE — THIS IS THE TOMB OF THE UNKNOWN GENDARME.

NO IT'S NOT — IT'S NOTRE DAME CATHEDRAL! OH, FRANCOIS, YOU'RE JUST PLAYING GAMES WITH ME...SO YOU CAN BUY ME A CUP OF COFFEE TO MAKE UP FOR IT!

That gave us the chance to have a proper chat.

But I had to dodge some tricky questions first...

ER...IT IS POSSIBLE YOU SAW ME ON THE BOAT FROM ENGLAND. I HAVE JUST BEEN TO SEE MY UNCLE — HE LIVES IN LIVERPOOL.

LIVERPOOL? THAT EXPLAINS THE WAY YOU SPEAK ENGLISH — YOU KNOW, YOU'VE PICKED UP A VERY STRONG ACCENT, FRANCOIS.

ANYWAY, IT WAS DEAD NICE OF YOU TO SHOW ME ROUND, BUT I KNOW IT MUST BE BORING FOR YOU. I'LL BE OFF BACK TO MY HOTEL NOW.

MAIS, NON! JULIE, I WILL NOT HEAR OF THIS — IT GIVES ME GREAT PLEASURE TO SHOW YOU MY CITY. THERE IS LOTS MORE TO SEE — S'IL VOUS PLAIT...

That means 'please', for those of you who don't speak the lingo.

WELL, IF YOU'RE SURE...TO TELL YOU THE TRUTH, THE ONE THING I MOST WANTED FROM THIS HOLIDAY WAS TO MEET A REAL FRENCHMAN.

THEN YOU HAVE BEEN A SUCCESS, JULIE — I AM AS FRENCH AS RED WINE AND SMELLY CHEESE!

We ended up spending the rest of the day together — and the next day, and the one after that.

Pete thought I was in big danger...

I'M GLAD YOU'RE HAVING A GOOD TIME, MATE — I JUST THINK YOU SHOULD BE CAREFUL, THAT'S ALL.

WHY? SHE THINKS I'M A PROPER FRENCHMAN, SO SHE'S HAPPY — AND I THINK SHE'S GORGEOUS, SO I'M HAPPY!

LISTEN, I KNOW YOU MEAN WELL, PETE — BUT I LIKE JULIE A LOT, AND I'M GOING TO SPEND AS MUCH TIME AS I CAN WITH HER.

BUT WHAT ABOUT WHEN WE ALL GO HOME, STUPID? YOU SAID SHE'S ALREADY TOLD YOU WHAT TRAIN SHE'S CATCHING — AND IT'S THE SAME ONE WE'RE GETTING ON!

WHAT ARE YOU GOING TO SAY WHEN SHE SEES YOU HEADING FOR LIVERPOOL?

I'LL WORRY ABOUT THAT WHEN IT COMES, MATE — IN THE MEANTIME, VIVE L'AMOUR! SEE YOU LATER, PETE.

Pete could never see things my w... could never forget about tomorr...

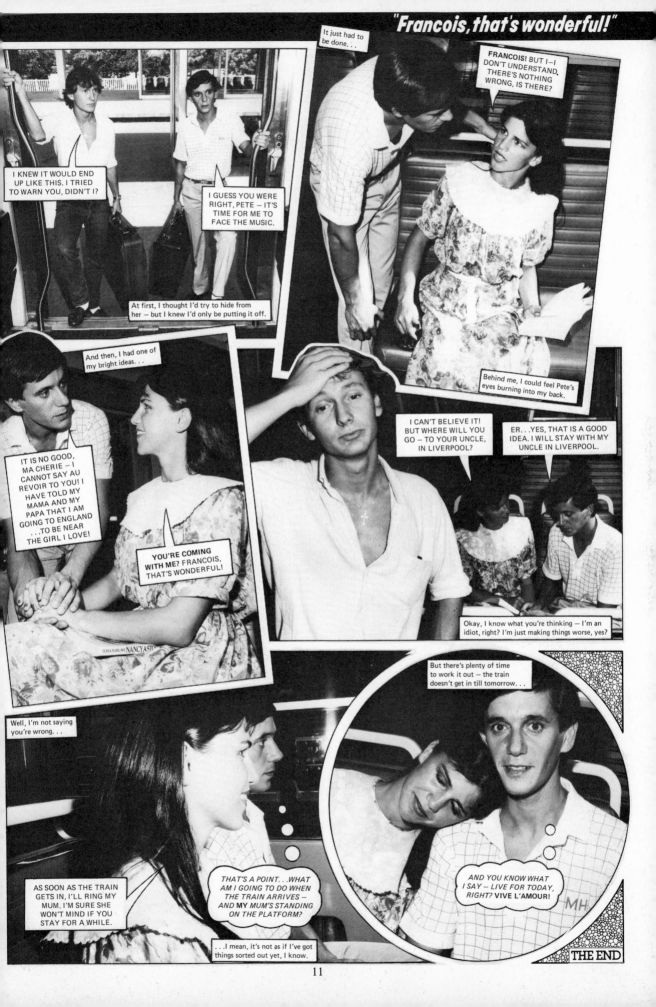

The A-Z of

A **ALTERED IMAGES.** A group who lived up to their name and changed from lovable lollipops to a smooth, sophisticated and respected pop band. The Altered Image in question really refers to lead singer Claire, who remains one of the best and best-known female pop stars.

B **DAVID BOWIE.** One of the most influential writers and performers of the last two pop decades. Bowie's work and imagery has coloured the sound and style of hundreds of followers from Gary Numan right through to the Human League.

Here it is, folks — the complete rundown on everything you ever wanted to know about the pop business — but didn't know who to ask . . .

D **DURAN DURAN.** The pop phenomena of the last couple of years, Duran Duran have inspired a fanatical following and a stream of John Taylor look-alikes as well as the predictable ''Biggest thing since the Beatles'' headlines. Their healthy mixture of artistic merit and shrewd business sense has helped keep them on top of the world.

E **EURYTHMICS.** And rhythm's what they've got. Featuring the startling looks and even more startling voice of the brilliant Annie Lennox, who must be one of the most talented women in pop. Ably partnered by one-time boyfriend Dave Stewart.

C **CULTURE CLUB.** Featuring a boy who looks like a girl and sounds like a great soul singer, Culture Club have successfully combined an outrageous image with good old-fashioned talent to become, deservedly, one of Britain's top bands, loved by teenagers and grannies alike.

F **FACTORY.** One of the most established and well-known of the small, independent record labels which have spawned so much fresh talent in recent years, and have challenged the multi-million major labels at their own commercial game. Factory's most successful signing is the cult band New Order.

G **GENESIS.** Fronted by the multi-talented Phil Collins, and before that, Peter Gabriel, Genesis have had the distinction of being a successful rock band through all the many changes in the pop world since the punk revolution shook up the heavy-rock orientated seventies. Originally formed by pop supremo Jonathan King — but I don't expect they like to shout about it.

H **HUMAN LEAGUE.** Undoubted masters of the synth-rock movement. Original line up included Martin and Ian from Heaven 17. When they left the group, singer Phil Oakey recruited Suzanne and Joanne from a local disco, and went on to chart success which eluded Ian and Martin for a long time to come.

I **IMAGINATION.** A vital ingredient in any successful pop band, and the name of one of the most successful Brit funk bands around.

J **MICHAEL JACKSON.** The most musical and successful member of a musical and successful family, Michael has been having hit records since he was a mere 11 years old. His beautiful voice and stylish dancing (not to mention his gorgeous looks) have kept the hits coming ever since.

K **KAJAGOOGOO.** The pop band who defied their critics, dumped their singer and still made successful records. Fronted by Nick Beggs, the Kajjers have remained down to earth and touchingly unaffected by their success and huge following.

Pop

Q STATUS QUO. More old favourites. The Quo have a following almost as dedicated as Duran Duran's, and though their style is timeless and unchanging, they keep on having those hits year after year.

R RESPOND. The record label set up by Paul Weller to encourage and promote new singing talent. "At the height of punk, every successful band was promising to do something for new talent," says Paul. "I'm keeping that promise."

L JOHN LENNON. One of the four most influential and successful musicians of all time: The Beatles (which really goes without saying). Lennon and McCartney went on to solo careers more successful than George or Ringo's, indicating that they formed the real song-writing talent behind the Beatles. Lennon was tragically murdered in 1980.

S SYNTHESISER. The instrument that changed the face of modern music — well, partly. It certainly spawned a whole new movement of bands. As a synth can reproduce the sound of most instruments, it became very popular for its versatility. Its disciples claim it's new and innovative, while its critics call it simply cold.

M MADNESS. The most lovable nutty boys in the business. Madness is the title of the group and of their theme single. It's also their general attitude to life. Who would disagree?

N GARY NUMAN. Gary Numan's career has been a strange one. Universally slated by music critics, he nevertheless sells records in their millions and plays to packed out venues when he tours. He has retired from live work several times, but can't seem to resist returning. His other claim to fame is as a rather dodgy aviator. Watch out for low-flying aircraft!

T TOYAH. A little lady with a mighty voice, Toyah is a pop star, successful actress and shrewd business woman. Her videos and live performances are imaginative and professional, and she claims to be happy only when she's working. Just as well, considering how busy she usually is.

W WHAM! George Michael and Andrew Ridgely form the nucleus of this highly successful pop combo, which first burst on the music scene with songs about life on the dole and the problems of being tied down too young. "We write about our own experiences and beliefs," says George. "I think that's why so many young people relate to our music."

X XTC. One of the most hardworking bands around, XTC are famous for playing long, hard, live tours and for the quirky eccentricity of their music, such as *Senses Working Overtime*. Headed by Andy Partridge, their uncompromising stance has built them a large cult following.

O ORCHESTRAL MANOEUVRES IN THE DARK. A weird name for a weird group. At least, that's how they've been dubbed. In fact, OMD are one of the most successful synthesiser bands, combining the rather cold, technical synth sound with haunting melodies and interesting lyrics.

U U2. A band with massive cult status both in their native Ireland and over here in England. Led by the lively and energetic Bono, they inspire fervour, dedication and wild enthusiasm in their huge following of fans.

Y PAUL YOUNG. Paul Young is one of the most down-to-earth and downright normal people you could wish — apart from his gorgeous soul voice, which has justly made him a star.

P POLICE. International megastars, pin-ups and millionaires, the Police have developed an original rock style which has made them extremely popular all over the world. They have a reputation for intelligence, and their records — superior commercial pop — reflect this.

V VIRGIN RECORDS. One of the most successful pop record labels, with signings including Culture Club, Human League and Heaven 17. Virgin have recently branched out into video games, book publishing and also own the London club, The Venue.

Z ZOO. The dance troupe on the BBC's golden oldie, *Top Of The Pops*, which still remains the most popular pop programme on TV, apart from stiff competition from the many new contenders, such as *The Tube*.

AFTER a quick peek at the strange collection of pictures printed below, photo stories will never seem quite the same again!

Here are the captions we really wanted to use at the time — but the nasty old Ed. wouldn't let us.

Still, we've always said that she's never had a great sense of humour . . .

WHEN I ASKED YOUR DAD FOR SOMETHING CHUNKY WITH LINKS FOR MY BIRTHDAY, I THOUGHT HE'D REALISED I MEANT A GOLD BRACELET!

I WISH THE CENTRAL HEATING ENGINEER WOULD HURRY UP. I'VE BEEN FROZEN IN THIS POSITION FOR THREE DAYS NOW!

DON'T BOTHER WITH HIM, LOVE. I'LL SHOW YOU WHAT **REAL** DANCING IS ALL ABOUT. ONE, TWO, THREE, SLIDE ONE, TWO, THREE, TURN. . .

. . .AND THEN I HAD SOME GARLIC MUSHROOMS WITH GARLIC BREAD. . .

FUNNIES!

THE YOUNG

He was one of the original

moody young rock stars in the 60's who went

on to become a slick, smooth pop star in the

70's and found a new lease of life in the 80's.

And he still doesn't look a day over 30!

LAST year, Cliff Richard celebrated 25 years in pop. He's one of the few performers to have successfully weathered the enormous changes in the music business since the heydays of the 60's and still retain his self-respect and the respect and loyalty of millions of fans worldwide.

"I've been very lucky," says Cliff modestly. "I don't know what else I would have done with my life, so it's just as well I've stuck around in music."

Cliff's being too casual. 'Stuck around' doesn't fairly describe his years of hard work and his polished professionalism — or his genuine love of music which has kept him fresh and enthusiastic even after a silver anniversary.

Cliff's career began way back in 1958, when he and his backing group, the Drifters (soon to become The Shadows) made up a demo tape for Columbia Records and landed themselves a recording deal. Their first single was a watered down Elvis impression called *Schoolboy Cruisin'*.

It didn't receive a lot of interest from critics or DJs, but the B side went down a storm. It was called *Move It* and got to number two in the charts!

Within a space of a couple of months, Cliff was The Face To Watch and became a prize pin-up all over the country. It's hard to believe now, but at the time, parents tried to ban Cliff's records and posters from their teenagers' rooms — because they thought he was too sexy! The parents' outrage only helped Cliff's popularity reach even greater heights and he went on to have a string of hits and to star in some classic films like *Livin' Doll* and *The Young Ones*.

By the late 60's Cliff had become deeply committed to his religious beliefs and he started to shake off his 'wild' image. In 1968, he appeared in the British Eurovision Song contest with *Congratulations*, which went straight to number one. However, his change of image had divided his fans, and it was to be his last chart-topper for 11 years. By Cliff's own admission he went on to make generally mediocre records during the early seventies.

"I almost lost interest because I was stuck in such an incredible middle-of-the-road bag," he has since admitted. But then, in 1976, came the album, *I'm Nearly Famous,* written largely by his old mate Bruce Welch. Suddenly, songs like *Miss You Nights* and *Devil Woman* were putting Cliff back in the charts and he was Big Time all over again. In 1979 the Cliff revival was confirmed with another number one with the haunting, *We Don't Talk Anymore.* He had shaken off his 'wholesome' image, but retained his faith.

"If being good is bad, then I'm going to try to be very bad indeed," he insists.

But in spite of his goody-goody image, Cliff has managed the seemingly impossible feat of appealing to young teeny-bopper girls as well as older women. After all, it's not every day you see teenagers and their mums screaming at the same bloke, is it? Not even Boy George could manage that!

So what's his secret? How has he stayed looking and sounding so incredibly young? Cliff just gives his famous enigmatic smile and replies:

"Rock 'n' Roll transcends age — it keeps you young!"

Obviously.

ONE!

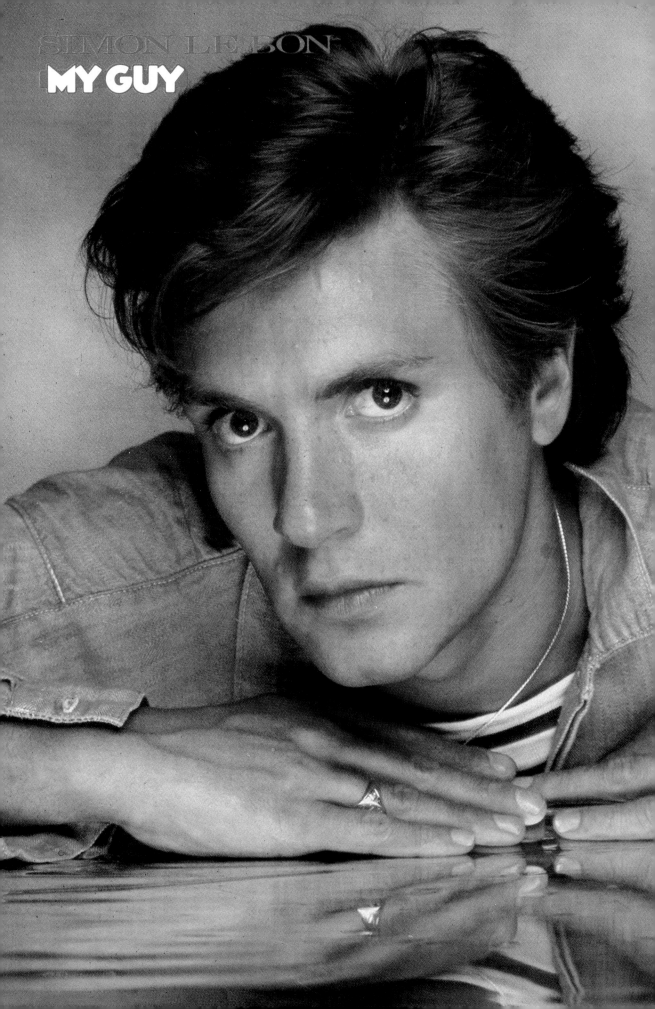

SIMON LE BON

MY GUY

ROGER
TAYLOR
MY GUY

Are You Getting ENOUGH?

Everyone does it, and everyone needs to do it for at least eight hours every day — but few of us actually do it enough.

What, you ask, are we talking about?

Sleep, of course!

HOW MUCH DO I NEED?

Everyone needs to sleep. But how much you actually need really depends on the individual. Some people need a full ten hours to feel really rested, while others feel really dopey on anything more than three or four hours a night. The amount you need really depends on how you feel. But most young people should aim for around eight hours a night.

A lot goes on while you're asleep. While you're sleeping, your muscles are at their most relaxed, and your blood is pumping around your body, replenishing your skin and hair as well as your internal organs. It's a time when moisturisers and skin lotions are more easily absorbed into the skin because the pores are fully relaxed. So you see, sleep can be good for your looks as well as your health.

And if you don't get enough sleep? Well, that can show in your looks as well. You may think it's great to stay out on the town into the early hours, but too many late nights can soon leave you with tense, hunched muscles, bloodshot eyes and dark circles under the eyes that no amount of make-up can fully get rid of. You'll also become irritable and begin to feel depressed.

WHAT IF I CAN'T?

Lots of people find it really hard to sleep at night. They spend hours tossing and turning and getting nowhere fast, until they begin to dread going to bed. But there are a few ways you can help yourself get a better night's shut-eye.

1. Don't eat before you go to bed, particularly cheese or fruit. Your body will keep you awake half the night, while it digests it. And steer clear of tea and coffee just before you turn in, too — these contain stimulants which can keep you awake.

2. Have a hot milky drink before you go to bed, to help you relax.

3. Sleep in a well-ventilated room. A hot, stuffy atmosphere can make it difficult for you to sleep. And you could wake up with a thick head!

4. Make sure you've got just enough covers. Too few will keep you awake with cold; too many will make you feel hot and heavy headed. A medium weight duvet is just right.

5. Try to relax. It's hard to do, but worrying too much over the events of the day, or the day to follow, can keep your mind alert and make it hard to sleep. Try doing some yoga (your local library will have details of classes), or reading a book or magazine to relax your mind.

GET UP AND GO!

There you are, sprawled across the settee watching Mum doing the ironing and listening to Dad snoring behind the paper. It's Sunday — all the shops are closed, your best mate's been dragged off to see her gran and there's nothing worth watching on the telly. So what do you do? Get on everyone's nerves with your moaning? Copy Dad and fall asleep? If you do, then you've only got yourself to blame for looking forward to *Songs of Praise*. **Take it from us, there are loads of things you can do to make your spare time pass in a flash and leave you to wonder where the weekend went!**

GET MOVING!

SWIM FOR IT!

The local pool is always open at weekends, so if you want to burn up a few thousand calories and work up an appetite for Sunday lunch, this is the thing to do. An added bonus could be the lifeguard — usually he's not bad looking. If you want to catch his eye, leave the arm bands at home.

CLEAR OUT!

This isn't as drastic as it sounds, we're only talking about clearing out all that old rubbish you've been hoarding in your room. You'll be amazed what you find when you disturb the top layer. Mum'll be delighted when she can see the carpet again and the local Oxfam shop will be pleased when you give them all your cast-offs!

BUS IT!

It won't cost you much to get on the first bus that comes along and stay on it till it reaches its final destination. You could end up somewhere really interesting — or, on the other hand, you could end up in the bus garage. Check this isn't a possibility!

PAMPER YOURSELF

Now's your chance to hog the bathroom and give yourself a top-to-toe beauty treatment. Start with a nice, long, relaxing bath full of bubbles! Slap on a face pack and lie there contemplating your navel! Don't soak for too long or you'll end up looking like a prune. Dry yourself thoroughly, then get down to the nasty business — defuzzing, cutting your toe nails, plucking your eyebrows, all the grotty jobs that need to be done. Finish off by washing your hair and giving it a good conditioning treatment. You'll feel great!

NOT TO DO WHEN YOU'RE BORED

with all the rotten jobs you won't help with.

5. Bite your nails — you'll regret it when you next want to paint them.
6. Phone your ex-boyfriend for a chat — you'll only feel a fool when he tells you he can't talk — his girlfriend's there.
7. Watch absolutely anything and everything that comes on the tele-

vision — all you'll end up with is square eyes and a massive headache.
8. Pick an argument with your brother or sister. It could turn nasty.
9. Start ringing all your friends, one after the other. Dad will go mad because of the phone bill.
10. Nothing!

10 THINGS

1. Over eat. You'll make yourself feel sick, fat and even more bored.
2. Tell everyone else how bored you are — then *you're* being boring.
3. Fall asleep. What a waste of time! You're entitled to the odd forty winks when you're eighty — not when you're eighteen!
4. Get under your mum and dad's feet when they're trying to get on

marathon. We're talking about a gentle jog round the block, borrowing your kid sister's skipping rope and having a skip round the park or having a go on a pair of roller skates, like you always threatened you would. Of course, it's more fun keeping fit with a fella, but if you haven't got a guy, this is a good way of nabbing one. Haven't you noticed just how worried about their appearance fellas are? They're always working out and working up a sweat. Oh, and don't worry — they don't always smell like that.

WALKIES

This one helps if you've got a dog. Rover will definitely be your best friend if you take him for a good long walk in the park. Like they say, a man's best friend is his dog, so you may bump into a few tasty fellas out walkies too!

PEDAL OFF!

Cycling is a great all-round exercise for firming and toning the muscles. Once you've got over the falling off stage, you'll be surprised at all the things you never noticed when you whizzed passed in the bus. Just a small point though, watch out for revolting little nine-year-old kids on BMXs — they'll try and make you fall off!

STUART
NEALE
MY GUY

How Well Do You Know Your Soap?

We all watch these weekly soap operas on TV.
But how well do you know what's going on?
Our quiz will sort out the regular viewer from the real addict!

1. Who was it Bet Lynch of *Coronation Street* once lived 'in sin' with:
a) Jack Duckworth?
b) Des Foster?
c) Mike Baldwin?

2. What was the name of the good-looking doctor Fallon from *Dynasty* had an affair with:
a) Steve?
b) Nick?
c) Mitch?

3. Barry Grant of *Brookside* once almost had a fling with one of the ladies in the close. Was it:
a) Michelle?
b) Petra?
c) Heather?

4. Lucy Ewing fell madly in love with a young fella called Mickey, who came to a rather nasty end.
How was he injured?
a) In an airplane disaster?
b) By a runaway horse on the ranch
c) In a car crash?

5. Which Ewing brother in *Dallas* is rarely seen at Southfork:
a) Larry?
b) Barry?
c) Gary?

6. Who was Diane of *Crossroads* once married to:
a) Carlos — the chef?
b) Chris — David Hunter's son?
c) Vince Parker — the postman?

7. What relation to Ken Barlow is Uncle Albert:
a) Uncle (by marriage)?
b) Father-in-law?
c) Father?

8. What is the name of Cliff Barnes' dumb blonde girlfriend?
a) Afton?
b) Donna?
c) Kristen?

More than 6 right:
Anyone who knows you would have guessed you'd do well at this quiz — your square eyes are a dead giveaway! Your life must revolve around watching soap operas. Just be careful that they don't become more real to you than life itself!

More than 3 right:
Well, you haven't shown yourself up too much, you've just proved that you could join in with the best of them when it comes to discussing Pam and Bobby's marriage problems or that wonderful outfit Heather was wearing in *Brookside* last week!

Less than 3 right:
Oh dear! Ever felt you might be missing out on something? Well, you have! Because as far as you're concerned soap's just something you wash with, not something to sit and watch week after week. Try tuning into the *Street* or *Brookside* one night — you'll never look back!

ANSWERS
1. c, *2.* b, *3.* b, *4.* c, *5.* c. Gary's regularly seen in **Knot's Landing**.
6. b and c. Vince Parker was her first husband.
7. b, *8.* a

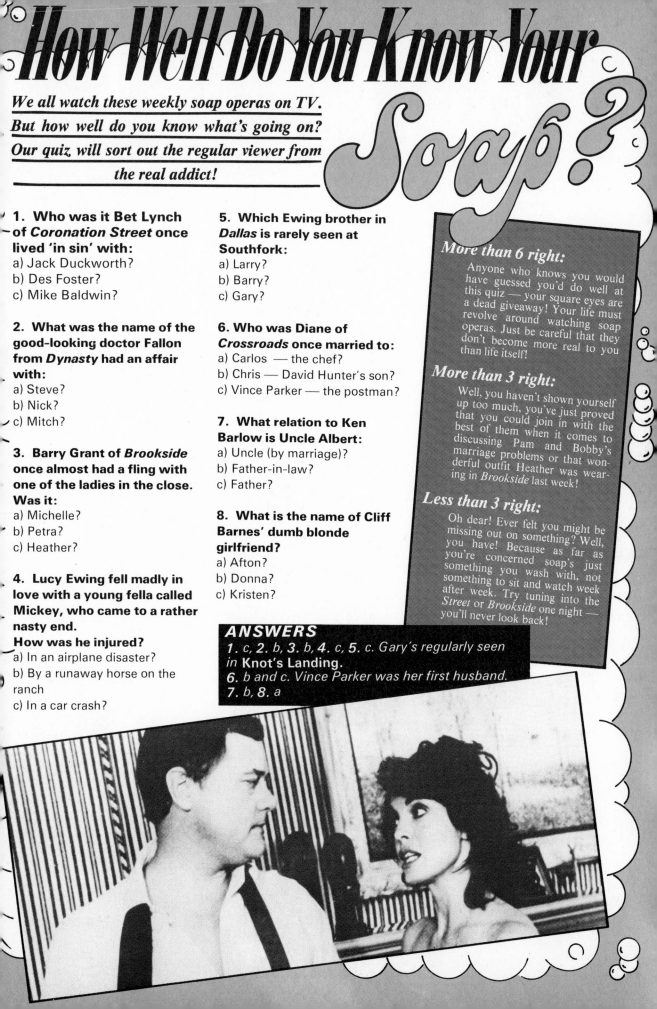

ARE YOU NICE T

Family, friends and fellas — like it or not, you have to spend most of your time with them, and your relationships with the people close to you are an important aspect of your life. So how do you cope with your nearest and dearest? Our quiz will tell you if you're playing fair . . .

SECTION 1

YOUR FAMILY

1 Your mum has been missing small amounts of money from her purse, and you suspect your little brother. Do you —
a) Tell Mum your suspicions immediately?
b) Warn your brother that you know what he's up to, and you'll tell Mum if he doesn't stop? \
c) Ignore the whole thing — let Mum and Bruv sort it out between themselves?

2 Your little sister keeps pinching your clothes and make-up. Do you —
a) Start locking your bedroom door whenever you go out?
b) Thump her the next time you catch her at it?
c) Bribe her by giving her small amounts of make-up, etc., for her own use — that way she should leave your stuff alone? /

3 You've just started a Saturday job, and your dad asks you to put some of your money towards household expenses. Do you —
a) Refuse — the small amount you get doesn't go very far as it is?
b) Do as you're told — even if you do think it's unfair? /
c) Compromise — and offer to pay for your own school dinners/bus fares, etc., with part of your money?

4 On the whole, do you think of your family as —
a) Something you're stuck with, so you just have to grin and bear it?
b) The only people you can really trust and rely on?
c) A solid foundation of people you love — when they aren't driving you up the wall? /

SECTION 2

YOUR FRIENDS

1 Your best friend has a bad reputation where guys are concerned, and as you go round with her a lot, part of it's rubbing off on you. Do you —
a) Drop your friend if you think the rumours have gone too far?
b) Stick by her and to hell with what other people say?
c) Carry on seeing her, but make sure you're seen with other friends as well? /

2 One of your mates has just bought a new, slinky black dress which she's really proud of. Trouble is, it makes her look enormous! Do you say —
a) "It makes you look enormous"? /
b) "I like you better in the grey shirt-waister?"
c) "You look fantastic"?

3 You have an exam at school, and your friend sits next to you so she can copy your answers. Do you —
a) Carefully cover up your paper so she can't see?
b) Let her copy if she really wants to? X
c) Tell her it will look too obvious as you'll both have the same answers and everyone knows you're sitting together?

4 On the whole, do you choose your friends for —
a) Loyalty — you like someone who will stick by you whether you're right or wrong?
b) Laughs — you like a mate with a good sense of humour who keeps you in stitches and who cheers you up when you're down /
c) Listening — the best friends are the ones you can tell all your troubles to?

26

O BE NEAR!

FELLAS

1 You fancy a guy you've known for ages, and you know he likes you too. Trouble is, he's too shy to do anything about it. Do you —
a) Forget him — if he liked you enough, he'd have asked you out no matter how shy he was? ✗
b) Give him as much encouragement as possible, and if he still doesn't ask you out, forget him?
c) Ask *him* out? ✓

2 Your fella is loving and sweet to you when you're alone, but he still acts like a big kid in front of his mates. Do you —
a) Ditch him — you're a girlfriend, not a babysitter?
b) Cause a scene whenever he starts being stupid and hope he soon stops?
c) Ignore it — you know how he really feels and that's all that counts? ✓

3 What, above everything else, would make you ditch a guy you really like?
a) Infidelity — you won't share him, and you could never forgive him if he went off with someone else?
b) Bad habits — if his breath smells and other people notice — it's time to say goodbye?
c) Thoughtlessness — if he cares more about going to see the local team on Saturday than he does about coming to see you, you're finished? ✓

4 What attracted you most to your most recent boyfriend?
a) Looks — he's gorgeous? ✓
b) Laughs — he's always the life and soul of the party?
c) Loneliness — he was there when you needed someone?

SCORES

SECTION 1	A	B	C		SECTION 2	A	B	C		SECTION 3	A	B	C
1	10	5	0		1	0	10	5		1	0	5	10
2	0	10	5		2	0	5	10		2	0	10	5
3	0	10	5		3	0	10	5		3	5	0	10
4	0	10	5		4	0	10	5		4	0	5	10

Add together the scores from all three sections.

0–45
On the whole, you're a selfish person. You like to have friends and feel popular, but you can't be bothered making too much of an effort to keep friends who start going off you, and you're rarely the first to apologise when you've argued. Your attitude to your family is the same — mostly take and no give, and so far, boyfriends have been more of a status symbol than anything else. You're quite hard and need to thaw out.

50–95
As usual, the middle category is the best one to come in. You're kind without being too extravagant and loyal without being biased. You have a lot of affection for the people you're close to, but it's not just blind devotion. You see their faults and have learnt to accept them and deal with them. You're honest to yourself and to others, and never deliberately hurtful. Just stay as you are and you'll never be without close friends.

100–120
You tend to be the clinging type. Maybe you're worried about not being popular enough — but you can't keep friends and fellas by never arguing with them and telling them only the things you think they want to hear. Don't be afraid to stand up for yourself. No relationship should cost you your self-respect.

GIRLS DON'T MAKE PASSES AT BOYS WHO...

Boys — want to know where you're going wrong with the girls? Here are some clues . . .

P.S. *If you're a girl who's ashamed of your fella, pass this over to him. He might get the hint!*

1. **Go round in gangs, shouting rude remarks at any girls they see.**

2. Think burping loudly in public is funny. (What a sense of humour!)

3. **Don't wear deodorant or aftershave because they think it's 'poofy'.**

4. Think they're John Travolta on the dance floor but look more like Lionel Blair.

5. **Think a woman's rightful place is in the home.**

6. Let you see yourself home.

7. **Have tiny, black hairs hanging out of their nostrils.**

8. Reckon Duran Duran are just a load of 'pretty boys' who can't sing. (Jealous . . .)

9. **Have already got a girlfriend — with a black belt in karate.**

10. Talk about football/rugby/cricket all the time.

11. **Think smoking makes them look big — all it does is give them bad breath.**

12. Wear a key ring loaded with keys hanging from their belt. Everyone knows the only key *he* needs is the one to his front door.

13. **Use hairspray, and never clean their brush or comb.**

14. Have bellies like Stan Ogden but reckon they've got the physique of Sylvester Stallone.

15. **Call girls 'Love', 'Doll' or 'Babe'.**

16. Still play with the train set Daddy bought them when they were six years old.

17. **Reckon taking you to the Wimpy is a good night out.**

18. Wear trousers that flap around just above their ankles.

19. **Wear vests when it's cold.**

20. Sell the details of their romances to the Press — well, school magazine, anyway.

28

MY GUY
COMPLETE
PHOTO
STORY

She wanted to be his girl. But they were....

JUST GOOD FRIENDS

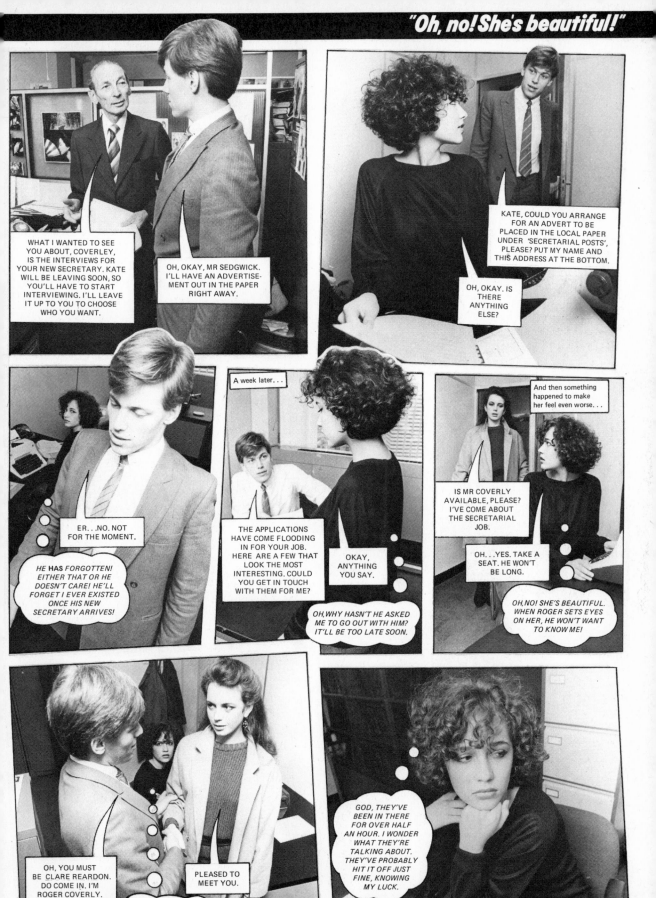

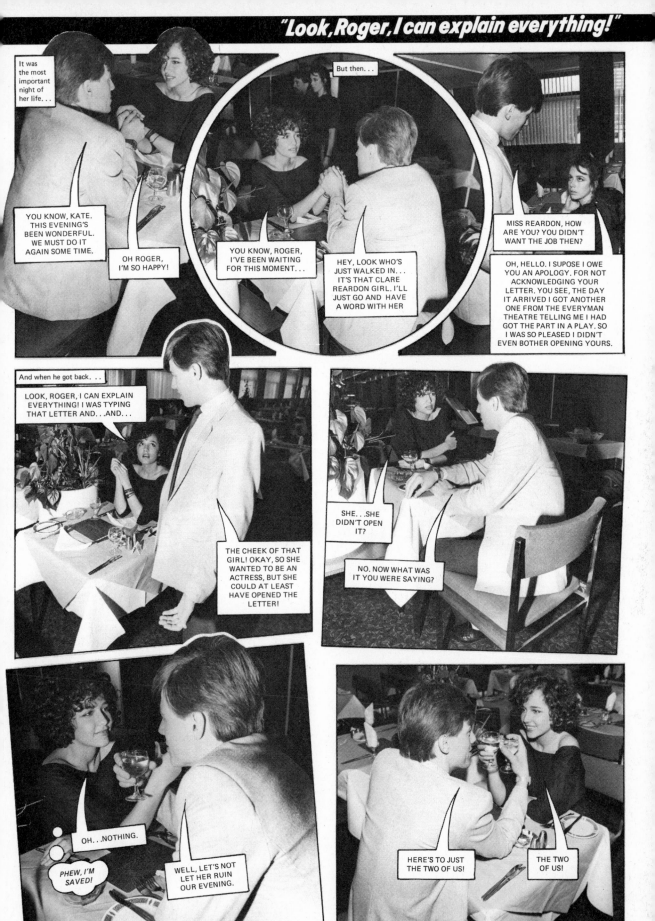

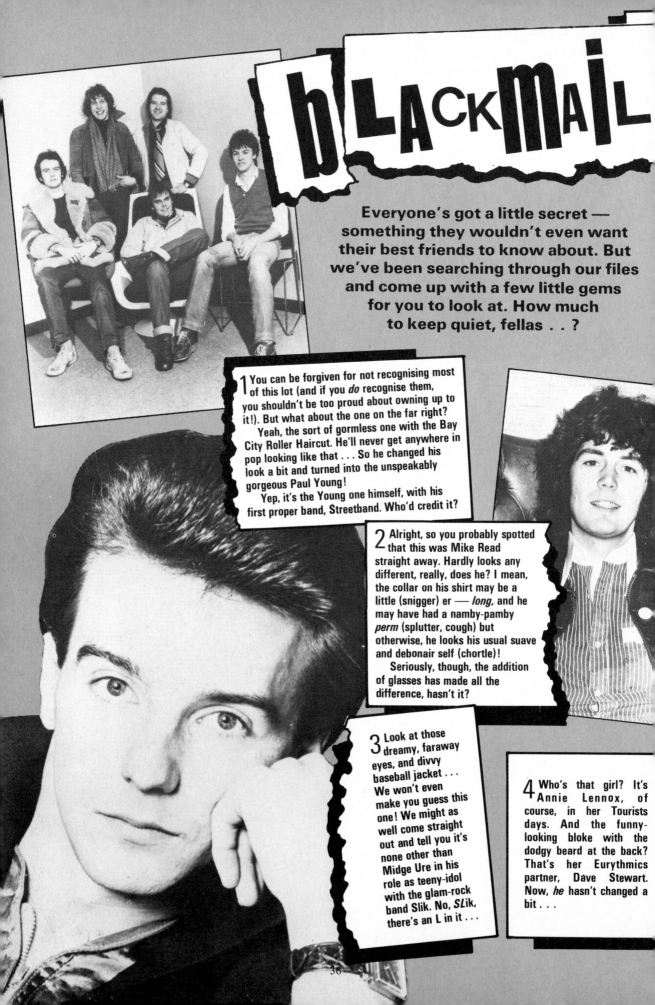

bLACKMAIL

Everyone's got a little secret — something they wouldn't even want their best friends to know about. But we've been searching through our files and come up with a few little gems for you to look at. How much to keep quiet, fellas . . ?

1 You can be forgiven for not recognising most of this lot (and if you *do* recognise them, you shouldn't be too proud about owning up to it!). But what about the one on the far right?

Yeah, the sort of gormless one with the Bay City Roller Haircut. He'll never get anywhere in pop looking like that . . . So he changed his look a bit and turned into the unspeakably gorgeous Paul Young!

Yep, it's the Young one himself, with his first proper band, Streetband. Who'd credit it?

2 Alright, so you probably spotted that this was Mike Read straight away. Hardly looks any different, really, does he? I mean, the collar on his shirt may be a little (snigger) er — *long,* and he may have had a namby-pamby *perm* (splutter, cough) but otherwise, he looks his usual suave and debonair self (chortle)!

Seriously, though, the addition of glasses has made all the difference, hasn't it?

3 Look at those dreamy, faraway eyes, and divvy baseball jacket . . . We won't even make you guess this one! We might as well come straight out and tell you it's none other than Midge Ure in his role as teeny-idol with the glam-rock band Slik. No, *SL*ik, there's an L in it . . .

4 Who's that girl? It's Annie Lennox, of course, in her Tourists days. And the funny-looking bloke with the dodgy beard at the back? That's her Eurythmics partner, Dave Stewart. Now, *he* hasn't changed a bit . . .

36

CORNER!

5 Now this is a really hard one. All of you there with freckles, spots and straggly hair who think you'll never develop a sense of style, take heart. The scraggy little girl in the left hand corner is none other than blonde bombshell Kim Wilde!

It's amazing what a few years and a bottle of bleach can do for a girl . . .

6 Oh, he'll die when he sees this . . . Remember The Leighton Buzzards? They went on to form Modern Romance and got all smooth and glossy. David Jaymes wasn't very glossy in this pic, though, was he? In fact, he looks downright rough. Lovable — but rough!

ARE YOU EATING

What you eat has a lot to say about the way you are. But a passion for curries doesn't mean you're hot stuff! There's more to it than that.

So put down that tempting pizza, pick up a pen and see how you score, 'cos our revealing quiz is going to give you plenty of food for thought!

1 When you're out with your pals you turn your nose up at hamburger and chips and keep your eyes glued on your diet sheet, but when you're alone is it a different story? Do you plonk yourself in front of the TV and reach for —
a. A family-size packet of crisps? /
b. A one-cal drink?
c. A diced carrot?

2 When you've had a row with your guy, do you reach for —
a. A box of Kleenex?
b. A box of chocs? /
c. Your make-up box?

3 That new guy's going all out to impress you with a first date at the best restaurant in town. It's at times like this you wish you hadn't skipped those French lessons, 'cos the only thing you understand is 'menu'! Do you —
a. Order number six and pray it's not snails in garlic?
b. Ask the waiter to explain what all the dishes are?
c. Say you're not hungry?

4 When your fella nips in to see you and asks 'What's cooking?', is it usually —
a. An oven full of cakes? /
b. A cup of tea?
c. Something foreign?

5 What's the nicest thing about having a holiday abroad? Is it —
a. Different fellas?
b. Different food? /
c. Different weather?

6 Would your perfect idea of a cosy, romantic night for two be —
a. Dinner at your local Chinese?
b. Dinner at home for two? /
c. Candlelight and violins?

7 When you see a really fat person, do you think —
a. Yeuk! What a disgusting sight? ✓
b. You ought to do your exercises more often?
c. You could do with a snack?

8 Which one of these nasty descriptions turns you off the most (if not all three)—
a. Pickled onion breath? /

b. Cigarette breath?
c. Garlic breath?

9 **If Simon Le Bon invited you out for a meal, would you order —**
a. The same as he does?
b. Oysters — they're supposed to be the food of love?
c. A steak?

10 **When you kiss your guy goodnight, are you thinking about —**
a. Him?
b. A late night snack?
c. Nick Beggs?

Before you tuck into those

answers about you and your

eating habits, try answering

a few tasty questions about

your man.

1 **If you dished up a cheese soufflé for his dinner, would he think you were —**
a. A clever girl?
b. Mad?
c. Trying to get rid of him?

2 **When he takes you out to eat, is it usually to —**
a. The cheapest place in town?
b. His mum's?
c. Anywhere his mates won't be?

3 **When it comes to cheffing, does your guy ever cook a meal for you —**
a. Occasionally?
b. Never?
c. Once, and never again?

4 **How does he feel about cuddly girls? Does he —**
a. Love 'em?
b. At seven stone you don't know the answer?
c. Seem to love 'em and leave 'em.

5 **What's his poison? Is it —**
a. Hamburgers?
b. Curries?
c. Home-cooked pizzas?

SCORE SCORE SCORE SCORE

For her						For him		
1. a 0 b 5 c10			6. a 5 b10 c 0			1. a10 b 0 c 5		
2. a 5 b 0 c10			7. a 0 b10 c 5			2. a 0 b 5 c10		
3. a 5 b10 c 0			8. a10 b 5 c 0			3. a10 b 0 c 5		
4. a 5 b 0 c10			9. a 5 b10 c 0			4. a10 b 0 c 5		
5. a10 b 5 c 0			10. a10 b 5 c 0			5. a 0 b 5 c10		

FOOD FOR THOUGHT

HERS

0–35: When anything unusual comes along you play it safe, you're so predictable. Yet deep down you're discontent and critical of others, while secretly you envy them their adventurous spirit. You've got to do something to get out of your rut and the first thing to do is stop telling yourself you're happy the way you are or 'what was good enough for your mum is good enough for you' — 'cos it isn't. Times have changed and you've got to change too or get left behind. Next time you go to order egg and chips, stop yourself and go for something different. It could be the start of a whole new recipe for life.

40–65: Not full marks, but full marks for trying. You're quite an insecure person but you're fighting against that impulse to hide yourself away. You're probably getting a bit on the tubby side and not surprisingly when you keep seeking solace in grub. When things get tough you reach for the cake tin, your mind's full of food instead of your future. Time you faced up to life without the help of the fridge!

70+: Life interests you in all its aspects. You're not afraid to try new things and that means you're not afraid to make mistakes. Things do embarrass you but you realise it's not the end of the world if you make a fool of yourself — and anyway, you can take it. You love a bit of romance but your heart's not ruling your head. Humour's important in your life too, and as for food it's just one more part of life that can be as interesting as you choose to make it. Why settle for an omelette when you could be trying caviar?

But adventurous and fun to be with as you are, there are times when you can be — dare we say it? — a little bit self-centred. You're so intent on having a good time yourself, you tend to forget other people and their problems. Not that you're cruel and heartless in any way — you're just a bit thoughtless. But you're lucky, in that friends and family don't seem to notice your little faults — you're too nice!

FOR HIM

0–15: Team up with this guy and if you're a low scorer yourself, you're doomed. He's as dull as ditchwater and as wet. If a boring cheapskate is your idea of Mr Right, then stick with him. If it isn't, then leave this one to his hamburger.

20–35: He's a real tryer, but you might think he's just trying! Dinner at his mum's isn't the Ritz but it does mean he's proud of you (and his mum). If you're a low scorer, he'll be a good influence. If you're both medium, you're okay for each other and if you're a top scorer, this one's worth working on.

40–50: Here's a guy that's not afraid to be different — liking nice, cuddly girls proves that! Taking you somewhere his mates won't see you doesn't mean he's ashamed of you, he just knows when to keep a good thing to himself. Make sure you keep him to yourself too!

FOOL FOR LOVE

It was love at first sight when Alan met Suzy. But would she ever return his feelings?

W HEN Suzy Marshall moved in down our road, I couldn't wait to get to know her. She was a stunner — slim, blonde, and beautiful — and every fella in the district was after her.

My heart used to sink every time some flash-looking fella pulled up outside her house in an equally flash-looking car.

Everything seemed to point to the fact that I didn't stand a chance. I mean, why should she be interested in someone who hadn't even left college and relied on a Saturday job for his spending money?

But luck was on my side for once when her mum started work at the local supermarket, sitting at the very next checkout to *my* mum. It wasn't long before they were the best of friends and Suzy and I were introduced.

BLUSH

"So you're Alan," she said, raising her eyebrows. "I've heard such a lot about you."

"Oh no," I cringed. "What's Mum been saying?"

"Just about how talented you are . . . the perfect son . . . always willing to help . . ."

Looking down at my feet I desperately tried to hide the crimson blush that was spreading rapidly up my neck and over my face, but when I looked up at her she was grinning, not taking the mickey at all and I burst out laughing.

I saw her quite a lot after that and we got on really well, chatting and laughing over silly jokes. But somehow I could never pluck up the courage to ask her out, so Suzy went on seeing her flash-looking boyfriends and I stayed in studying for my exams.

For six months we carried on like that and each time I saw her I fell more in love with her.

She was the first person I broke the good news to when I got the job as trainee car mechanic at the local garage and I could tell she really was pleased for me.

"That's great," she said, enthusiastically. "I'm really pleased for you. Soon you'll be earning as much money as I do."

KISSED

Suzy had a good job as an audio typist and I knew she took home a good salary. That was obvious just from the clothes she wore. So when she knocked on my door one day and said she'd bought a car I wasn't surprised.

"The guy I bought it from said it

"I've heard such a lot about you," she said.

might need tuning," she said as she proudly showed me the Mini parked outside her house. "I don't suppose you could do that for me, could you? I'll take you for a drive afterwards!"

"Of course," I nodded. "It's no trouble."

All afternoon I worked on that car, determined to have it ready for Suzy,

and true to her word she took me out in it that evening.

I don't think I've ever enjoyed myself so much, and when she kissed me goodnight, I thought I'd burst with happiness. At last I'd managed to impress her with something, and look how it had paid off!

I often did work on her car after that, tuning the points, touching up the paintwork or treating it for rust. I quite enjoyed those afternoons I spent working on the car, and I thought Suzy did too because she was always there to pass me the tools I needed and afterwards we often went for a meal.

Eventually the car was in perfect condition and even if I say so myself, I was pleased with the results. As for Suzy, she was delighted.

LOVE

Every night I saw her going out in it, but she never asked me along. Weeks turned into months and the nearest I got to her was to wave across the street as she drove past.

It wasn't too long before I realised Suzy hadn't fallen in love with me at all — she'd been using me and now that her car was in perfect condition I wasn't needed. It hurt knowing that, it hurt a lot. But last night she came round, eyes brimming with tears saying she'd backed her car into a wall. Could I sort it out for her?

There's no need to tell me I'm a fool, I know I am. But today as I started work on her car and she stood there watching, I felt happy. Being used by her is better than not seeing her at all.

This way at least there's a chance — a slim chance that one day she'll love me the way I'll always love her.

PERSONAL

My Guy
Kings Reach Tower
Stamford Street
London
SE1 9LS

That's what this guy was at pains to tell everyone when our model draped herself over him. Looks like she's had one too many *Lucozades!*

SHE'S NOT WITH ME!

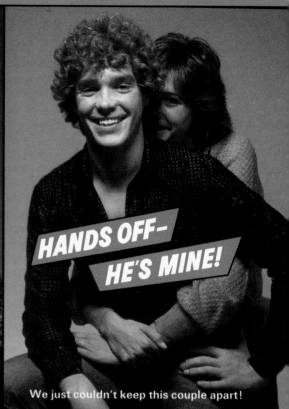

HANDS OFF– HE'S MINE!

We just couldn't keep this couple apart!

A-A-ATISHOO!

Sneezes always come at the most inopportune moments!

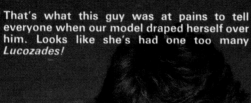

oks like this girl's got something to hide — er face. Maybe she daren't risk her boyfriend eing her in the arms of another guy!

How to get your guy — keep him in a strangle hold!

NO PUBLICITY, PLEASE...

THE BIG DADDY SCHOOL OF DATING

Smile, we said — and look at the face she pulled! Maybe she had something against our photographer . . .

IF LOOKS COULD KILL ...

BE YOUR MAKE-UP

Learn the tricks of the trade!

TO make those unwanted spots disappear (yes, even models have spots), apply concealer stick under your foundation. Blend it into the area over and around the spot, then apply foundation with a damp cosmetic sponge. Top with a dusting of transluscent powder for a flawless finish.

*Get rid of dark circles under the eye with white eye pencil. Smudge it gently over the circles, then apply foundation in the usual way.

*Give yourself a thinner face by applying blusher in a diagonal line from your temple along your cheekbone so that it is just level with the middle of your eye. Then add a very slight touch of brown eyeshadow just under your cheekbone close to your ears. It'll give an instant 'hollow' look.

*Get rid of a double chin by lightly dusting blusher under your chin, and highlighting your temples and the tip of your nose, with pale face highlighter.

*To make eyes look less bloodshot, line the inner rims with white eye pencil. It'll make them seem bigger, too.

*An essential ingredient in every make-up bag must be gold eyeshadow. Don't be put off, it's not as exotic as it sounds — a small dot applied to the centre of your lids makes your eyes seem much bigger and more wide-awake.

*Make close-together eyes seem further apart by applying a lighter shade of eye colour in the inner corners of your eyes, with a darker shade winging out towards the browbone.

*To make wide-set eyes seem closer together, use a darker shadow on the inner corners, with a lighter shade in the socket line.

*Treat yourself to some eyelash curlers. They'll make your eyes look bigger and better than mascara ever can. And on the subject of mascara, stop it clogging by separating your lashes with a clean, dry mascara brush after every coat.

*Make thick lips seem thinner with a dark, matte shade of lip colour. Avoid pearlised shades and lip glosses — they'll just draw attention to your mouth.

*Make small lips more appealing by outlining the shape with a lip pencil.

*Give yourself an extra kissable mouth by adding a top of gold eyeshadow to the centre of your upper lip. Believe it or not, it's very subtle — and sexy!

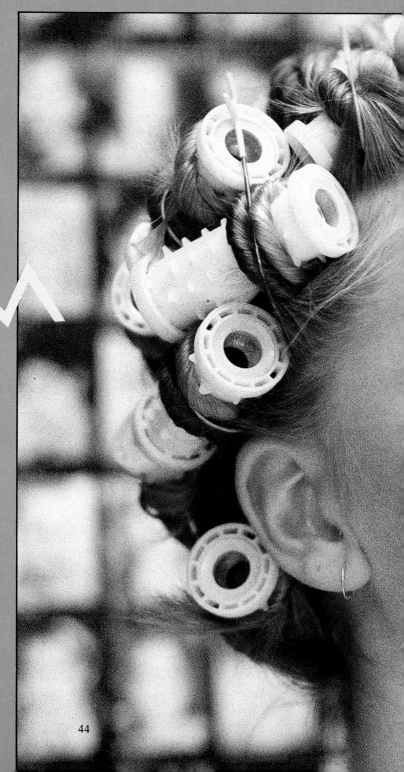

OWN ARTIST!

BLANCMANGE
MY GUY

STEVE
NORMAN
MY GUY

LD
302

LEROY JOHN
MY GUY

WHAM!
MY GUY

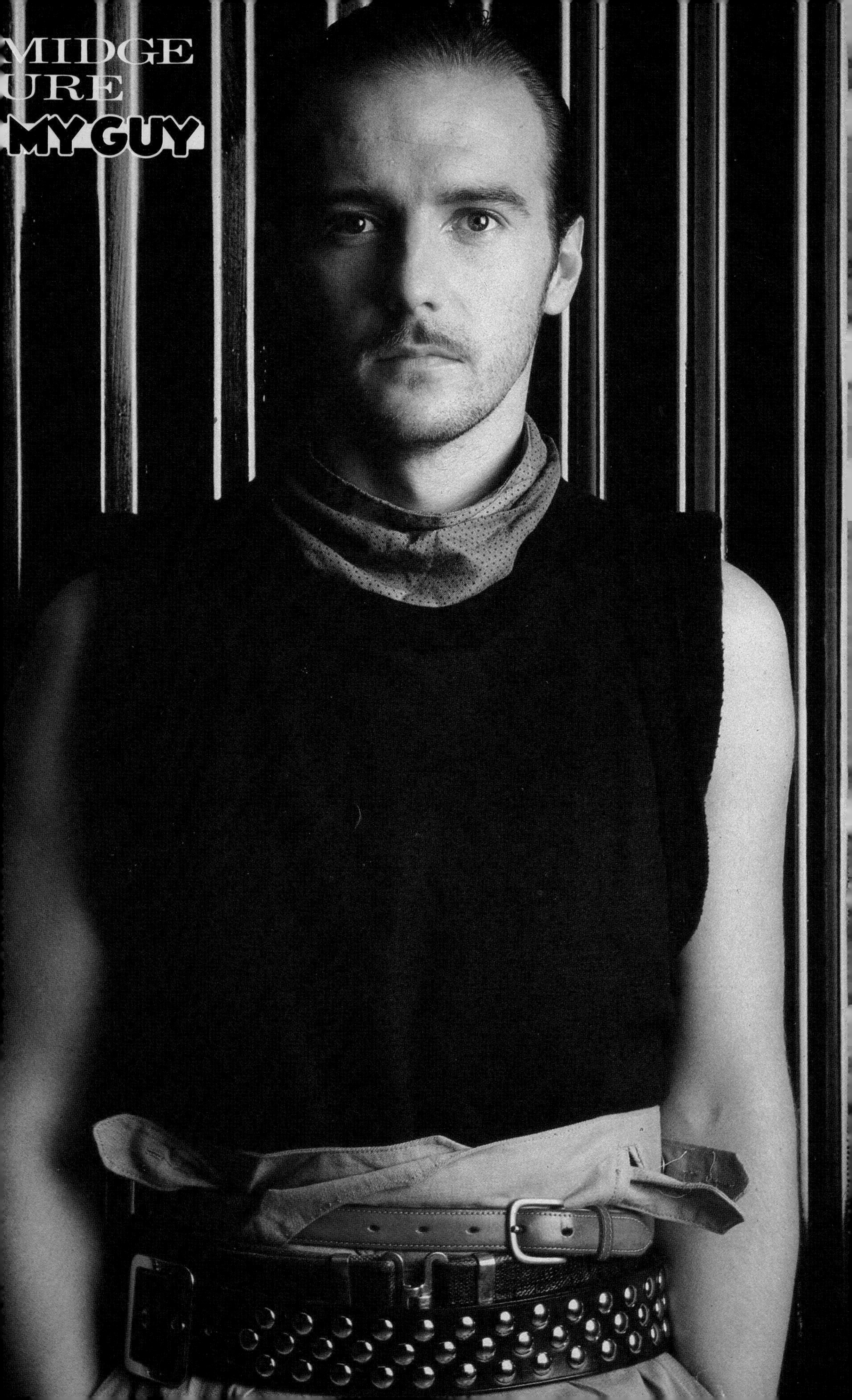
MIDGE
URE
MY GUY

LOOKING GOOD-

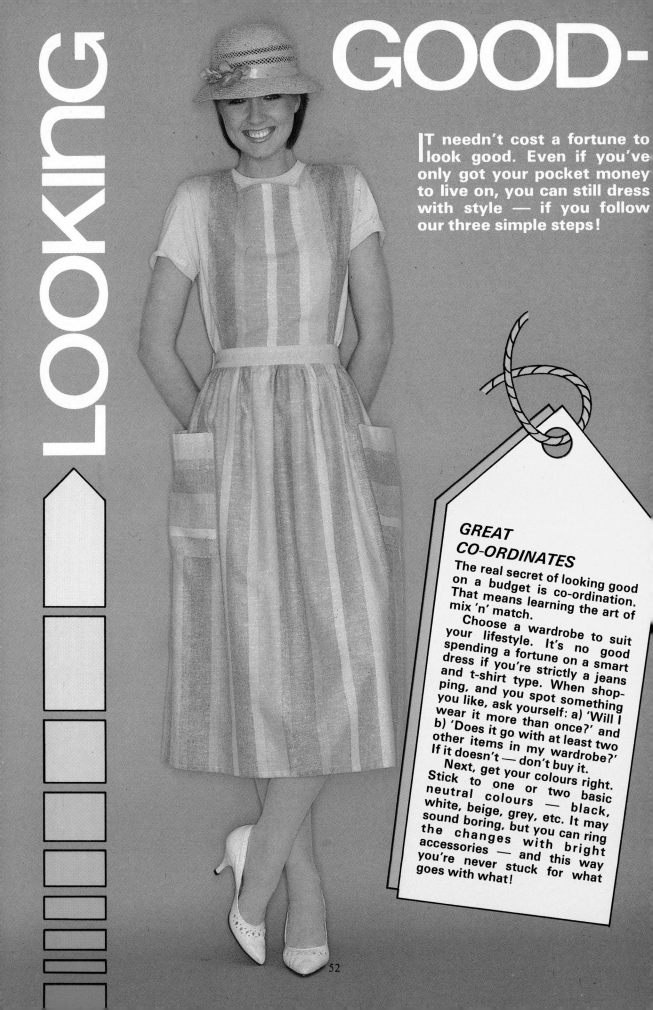

IT needn't cost a fortune to look good. Even if you've only got your pocket money to live on, you can still dress with style — if you follow our three simple steps!

GREAT CO-ORDINATES

The real secret of looking good on a budget is co-ordination. That means learning the art of mix 'n' match.

Choose a wardrobe to suit your lifestyle. It's no good spending a fortune on a smart dress if you're strictly a jeans and t-shirt type. When shopping, and you spot something you like, ask yourself: a) 'Will I wear it more than once?' and b) 'Does it go with at least two other items in my wardrobe?' If it doesn't — don't buy it.

Next, get your colours right. Stick to one or two basic neutral colours — black, white, beige, grey, etc. It may sound boring, but you can ring the changes with bright accessories — and this way you're never stuck for what goes with what!

SPENDING

Less!

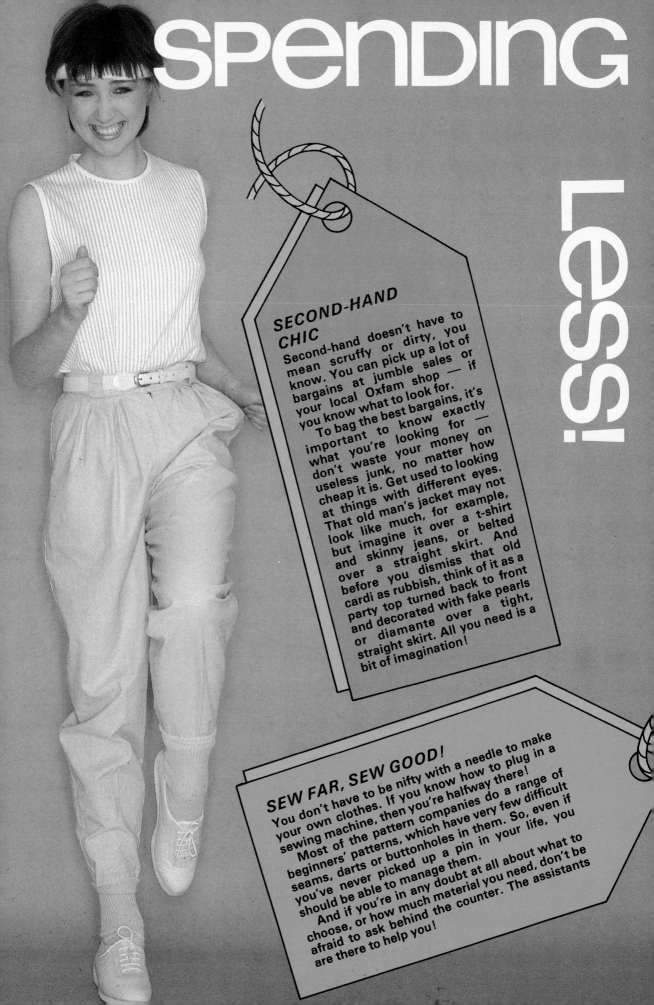

SECOND-HAND CHIC

Second-hand doesn't have to mean scruffy or dirty, you know. You can pick up a lot of bargains at jumble sales or your local Oxfam shop — if you know what to look for.

To bag the best bargains, it's important to know exactly what you're looking for — don't waste your money on useless junk, no matter how cheap it is. Get used to looking at things with different eyes. That old man's jacket may not look like much, for example, but imagine it over a t-shirt and skinny jeans, or belted over a straight skirt. And before you dismiss that old cardi as rubbish, think of it as a party top turned back to front and decorated with fake pearls or diamante over a tight, straight skirt. All you need is a bit of imagination!

SEW FAR, SEW GOOD!

You don't have to be nifty with a needle to make your own clothes. If you know how to plug in a sewing machine, then you're halfway there!

Most of the pattern companies do a range of beginners' patterns, which have very few difficult seams, darts or buttonholes in them. So, even if you've never picked up a pin in your life, you should be able to manage them.

And if you're in any doubt at all about what to choose, or how much material you need, don't be afraid to ask behind the counter. The assistants are there to help you!

DURAN DURAN

MY GUY

Recipes For Success
IT'S ONLY NATURAL!

*O*UR grandmothers knew a thing or two about natural beauty. That's why they didn't spend a fortune on expensive cosmetics, but relied instead on nature's own beauty secret — herbs.

You can buy a wide range of herbs now in supermarkets or health-food stores, or visit your local gardening centre for seeds and grow your own. Either way, herbs provide a natural and inexpensive way towards a beauty that is more than just skin deep.

The only real way to find the ones best for you is to mix them about and make up your own creams and face masks until you get the results you want. But as this takes time and a lot of testing, we've put together a few general, well-tried tips and recipes to get you started on your way to natural beauty!

STEAMING

This is a good method of opening the pores before applying a face pack, or just to clear them out. If you want to clean and soothe your skin, add a handful of camomile, nettle, rosemary or thyme to the steaming water. If your skin is greasy, yarrow (available from health stores) will help to dry it out, while peppermint or elderflower will help tighten your skin, and leek is good for mild acne.

EXFOLIATING

This is the name given to rubbing away the dead surface skin and leaving a healthy glow. It's good to try about once a week for normal to dry skin, or more often for oily complexions.

Try rubbing natural sea-salt on a face-flannel as a natural way, or papaya mint tea is excellent for removing surface skin debris. Buy the tea in tea-bags from your local health-food shop, make up a cup and soak a flannel in it. Then apply the hot flannel to your face and repeat a few times. Your skin will soon notice the difference!

FACE PACKS

A good face pack for all skin types is one made from parsley, which is very cheap, widely available and can be easily grown outside or indoors.
Put two handfuls of fresh parsley in boiling water, and boil for two minutes. Strain, and stir in a tablespoon of honey and one egg yolk, when the mixture has cooled. Brush on face and leave for 15 minutes. Rinse off with tepid water.

Or try this excellent herbal cream — it's especially good for clearing up spots!

Take: 2 pints of rose-water, 2 sliced apples, 2 tablespoons of chopped fennel and celery, a pinch of barley meal, three egg whites and a teaspoon of lanolin. Put the rose-water, apple, fennel, celery and barley meal in a double saucepan or in a bowl over a pan of boiling water and simmer. When the mix goes mushy, add the rest of the ingredients. Beat until smooth and keep fresh in the fridge. The results make the effort well worthwhile!

SKIN TONICS

You can make lots of simple and refreshing toners yourself. This one is very easy to make and lovely to use.

Take: 2 cups of raspberries, 1 cup of rose petals, a teaspoon of honey and 2 pints of cider vinegar. Put the first three together in a covered pot for a month covered by the vinegar. Strain, dilute with equal parts of distilled water for a refreshing toner.

You can even make your own perfume! Try this one — it has a spicy, tangy fragrance.
Boil together: 2 cups of rose-water, 2 cups cider vinegar, 2 bay leaves and $\frac{1}{2}$ tablespoon of crushed cloves. Allow to mature for a month before using.

If you've tried any of our recipes and like them, we hope you'll be encouraged to try your own. If you find the recipes unsuitable, you can always modify them — adding ingredients you particularly like to suit your own tastes. Develop your own individual cosmetics; they'll be as unique as you are!

57

GOLDEN

Test your knowledge of chart history with our bumper Golden Oldies quiz. Some will be easy, provided you've got a good memory — and some may need a little help from Mum and Dad! Anyone who scores over 17 is a Modern Music Mastermind!

1 Who had a hit with *You'll Never Walk Alone* in 1963?

2 They put another brick in the wall in 1979 and got to number one with their first hit single in $12\frac{1}{2}$ years! Who are they?

3 Cliff Richard is one of the original 'golden oldies'. What does he have in common with comparative newcomer Gary Numan?

4 Who were *Not In Love* in 1975?

5 Who was the podgy rock 'n' roll star who invented *The Twist*?

6 Which group had their early success with three singles with very similar titles — *All Around The World*, *The Modern World* and *News Of The World*?

7 Songs with *Xanadu* in the title have been big hits twice in Britain. Once in 1968 and once in 1980. Can you name the singers of both songs?

8 Who was the *Long-Haired Lover From Liverpool* in December 1972?

9 *Shaddup You Face* was a novelty number one hit for who in 1981?

10 Who pretended to have their first hit with *Stop Your Sobbing* at the beginning of 1980?

11 What film included the hits, *How Deep Is Your Love*, *Staying Alive* and *If I Can't Have You*?

12 Kate Bush's first single release, based on a famous story, went straight to number one. What was it called?

13 Who was *Lost In France* a long time ago and later had *A Total Eclipse Of The Heart*?

14 Gary Tibbs was bass player with two hugely successful but very different bands. What were they called?

15 David Bowie had a big hit with *Space Oddity*, which featured the astronaut Major Tom. Bowie was to mention Major Tom again in a later number one. What was it called?

OLDIE - POP QUIZ

16 Kim Wilde adopted her famous dad's showbiz surname for her own career, but what is her real surname?

17 Cliff Richard released an album called *Silver* in 1983. Why did he give it that title?

18 David Essex has combined pop stardom with an acting career. Name the two films in which he played Jim McLaine?

19 John Travolta and Olivia Newton John scored two number one hits from the film *Grease*. What were the songs?

20 In what year was *The House Of The Rising Sun* a hit for the Animals — first time around?

21 Diane Earle is the real name of which hugely successful ex-Motown singing star?

22 Who sang *You've Lost That Loving Feeling* in 1965?

23 *Don't Go Breaking My Heart* was a number one hit in 1976 — for which two singers?

24 Whose camera never lied in 1982?

25 Did you know there has been a Top Ten version of *The Lion Sleeps Tonight* every ten years since 1962? Whose turn was it to take it into the charts in 1982?

ANSWERS

1. Gerry and The Pacemakers.
2. Pink Floyd.
3. Both their original surnames are Webb.
4. 10 cc.
5. Chubby Checker.
6. The Jam.
7. 1968 — Dave, Dee, Dozy, Beaky, Mick and Titch. 1980 — Olivia Newton John with the Electric Light Orchestra.
8. Jimmy Osmond.
9. Joe Dolce.
10. The Pretenders.
11. *Saturday Night Fever.*
12. *Wuthering Heights.*
13. Bonny Tyler.
14. Roxy Music and Adam And The Ants.
15. *Ashes To Ashes.*
16. Smith.
17. He had just celebrated 25 years in pop — his silver anniversary.
18. *That'll Be The Day* and *Stardust.*
19. *Summer Nights* and *You're The One That I Want.*
20. 1964.
21. Diana Ross.
22. The Righteous Brothers.
23. Elton John and Kiki Dee.
24. Bucks Fizz.
25. Tight Fit.

MARKED PERSONAL

It seemed everyone had a boyfriend except Angela. Somehow she had to get one . . . she just had to!

I WAS DESPERATE FOR A FELLA!

SITTING in front of the dressing table mirror doing my make-up, I was determined that tonight would be different. Tonight I wouldn't go home from the disco alone, I'd be walked home by some dishy fella who'd danced with me all night and kissed me gently as he said goodbye.

But chucking my lipstick down with a sigh, I knew the chances of me getting off with anyone were slim.

Downstairs I could hear my younger sister shouting goodbye to Mum and Dad as she went out to meet her boyfriend, and out of all my friends who'd be down at the disco only three of them didn't have fellas of their own — and they never had any trouble finding someone to take them home. It was always me, mousey little Angela Burton who got left behind, who never got asked to dance and who always cried herself to sleep at night.

The next day at school all the others would talk about what they'd got up to at the disco, and I could tell they felt sorry for me when I buried my head in a book so I wouldn't have to admit I'd gone home alone — again.

But tonight was going to be different — no matter what I had to do I was going to have a boyfriend by the end of the evening!

GASPED

Squeezing myself into the tightest pair of jeans I had, I reached for the new top I'd bought. It was very skimpy, and I knew Mum would have a fit if she saw how low it was cut. But it wasn't too hard to sneak out without her seeing me and before I had a chance to think about what the others would say, I was at the disco.

"Angela," gasped Sue, as I handed my jacket in at the cloakroom. "You look so different! All that make-up — and you've curled your hair . . ."

I smiled, trying to hide the butterflies leaping about inside me. "What do you think of the top? Not too revealing, is it?"

"Er . . . no," she stammered. "It's really, well — really eye-catching."

"Coming for a dance?" I asked quickly, before my courage ran out, and I hid in the ladies.

"All right," she nodded.

I could tell everyone was looking at me as I twirled and spun my way round the dance floor. Normally I never got out of my chair and now I was the star of the show! It felt great to really let myself go to the music, just like I saw the others do week after week. When the record finished

I was flushed and gasping for breath.

"That was great," I panted, as Sue made her way to the bar to get us a couple of Cokes. But before she could reply, a fella stepped in between us, blocking my way. My heart almost stopped as he looked me straight in the eyes and said:

"Would you like to dance?"

"Yes," I said quickly, too quickly, "I'd love to."

SHAKING

The record was a slow one, and as he took me in his arms I was so nervous I was almost shaking. He held me so tight, so close, I could hardly breathe. But his aftershave smelt nice, and after a while I leant my head on his shoulder and sighed with happiness. At last, I'd be able to join in when the girls at school talked about the disco — because I really had something to talk about!

One slow, dreamy number drifted into another and still we danced.

"My name's Tony," he murmured into my ear eventually.

"I'm Angela," I gulped. "Angie."

"Let's go for a walk," he whispered. "It's getting hot in here."

Leading me by the hand, he pushed his way through the crowds to the door. Over in the corner I could see several of my friends and I smiled triumphantly as I followed Tony outside.

For a while we walked down the road in silence. It felt cold after the heat of the disco, and I shivered.

"Cold?" asked Tony. I nodded, too nervous to say anything.

"I'll soon warm you up," he breathed, and pushing me up against a wall he kissed me.

I was so shocked that at first I couldn't do anything, but gradually I relaxed and responded as his soft lips met mine. At that moment I was the happiest girl alive, but gradually his kisses changed, they were hard and demanding and hurt my lips.

"No — no," I gasped, trying to push him off. But he was too strong and before I could stop him, I could feel his hand tearing at my top.

Tears streamed down my face as I struggled to get away. Grabbing his hair, I yanked it back as hard as I could.

"You bitch!" he gasped.

Sobbing, I pushed past him.

"Why bother dressing like a tart if you don't want to behave like one?" he shouted after me.

His words rang in my ears as I ran down the road and I didn't stop running until I was safely indoors.

*"I'll soon warm you up,"
he breathed.*

In the bathroom I scrubbed all my make-up off and brushed my hair until it was straight — and as for the top, I threw that straight in the bin.

TROUBLE

As awful as he may have been, Tony taught me something that night, something important, to be yourself. I was a fool to act the way I did just to get a fella. All I got was a whole lot of trouble and I know it could have got a lot worse.

Now when I go to the disco I sit watching the others smooching with their fellas and it doesn't bother me.

There's nothing wrong with being quiet and shy and on your own, nothing at all. And one day I know I'll meet a fella I really can get on with, someone who likes me just the way I am. There's no hurry, because now I'm not afraid to be alone.

Personal

My Guy,
Kings Reach Tower,
Stamford Street,
London SE1 9LS.

Is Chris After Ann—or her money?

JUST A GIGOLO?

LOOK, SUE, ISN'T IT LOVELY? I THINK I'LL GET IT FOR DAD.

BUT IT'S NOT HIS BIRTHDAY, IS IT?

NO, BUT HE **COULD** DO WITH A NEW SHIRT. . .

YOU'RE HOPELESS WITH MONEY, ANN! IF YOU'VE GOT ANY, IT JUST BURNS A HOLE IN YOUR POCKET 'TILL IT'S SPENT!

But Ann never seemed to learn that lesson.

ER, SUE, D'YOU THINK YOU COULD PAY MY BUS FARE? I SEEM. . .ER. . .TO HAVE RUN OUT OF CASH.

SO WHAT'S NEW? C'M[...] PUT YOUR PURSE AW[...] I THINK I CAN SEE [...] BUS COMING.

Ann's sister, Lisa, was waiting for her back home.

HI, ANN! BEEN OUT BLOWING YOUR WAGES AGAIN? OH, AND BEFORE I FORGET, A LETTER CAME FOR YOU THIS MORNING — MUM LEFT IT IN THE KITCHEN.

I HOPE IT'S NOT FROM THE CATALOGUE COMPANY. I KNOW I'M TWO WEEKS BEHIND WITH THE PAYMENTS, BUT I WAS GOING TO SEND THEM A CHEQUE TOMORROW.

THANKS, LISA.

But the letter wasn't from the catalogue company. . .

I — I DON'T BELIEVE IT!

. . .it was a letter to tell her her premium bond had come up — and she'd won £300

Later that night, Ann met Sue to c[...]

. . .IT'S SOLVED ALL MY MONEY PROBLEMS, SUE — AND I'LL EVEN BE ABLE TO GO TO PARIS NOW. YOU KNOW HOW I'VE ALWAYS WANTED TO GO TO PARIS. . .

. . .BUT NEVER HA[...] THE MONEY BEFOR[...] LOOK, ANN, I HATE [...] BE A WET BLANKE[...] BUT WILL YOU REALLY BE ABL[...] TO SAVE?

LOOK, IT'LL BE DIFFERENT THIS TIME, SUE. I KNOW I'M NO GOOD WITH MONEY, BUT EVEN I CAN'T SPEND THREE HUNDRED POUNDS OVERNIGHT!

WELL, WE'LL SEE. BUT PROMISE ME YOU WON'T CASH THE CHEQUE JUST YET.

ER. . .I CAN'T DO THAT. . . I WENT TO THE BANK THIS AFTERNOON.

OH, ANN, I DON'T THINK YOU'LL EVER LEARN HOW TO HANDLE MONEY!

Just then. . .

HI, SUE, I DIDN'T KNOW YOU WERE HERE!

CHRIS, I HAVEN'T SEEN YOU SINCE. . .WELL, I CAN'T REMEMBER WHEN! I DIDN'T EVEN KNOW YOU WERE BACK IN TOWN!

ER, SUE. . .

OH, SORRY, ANN. CHRIS, THIS IS ANN DAWSON, MY BEST MATE AND ALL ROUND LOONY. WE'RE OUT CELEBRATING 'COS HER PREMIUM BOND'S JUST COME UP.

HI, ANN. TELL ME. HOW DID YOU COME TO MEET MY FAVOURITE COUSIN?

Sue went off to get them more drinks and Ann stayed behind to talk to Chris.

But they were soon beyond party pleasantries.

. . .AND WHEN YOUR MONEY RAN OUT SO DID THE CUSTOMERS?

THAT'S RIGHT. MY MATE AND I JUST DIDN'T HAVE THE CASH TO KEEP GOING. IT WAS A SMALL BUSINESS — A BIKE MESSENGER SERVICE AND THE BANK DIDN'T THINK WE WERE WORTH TAKING A RISK ON.

ANYWAY, ENOUGH OF THAT — THIS IS MEANT TO BE A PARTY. HOW ABOUT A DANCE?

I'D LOVE TO!

I'VE GOT THE FEELING THAT I'M GOING TO BE SEEING A LOT OF CHRIS FROM NOW ON. I HOPE SO. . .I REALLY HOPE SO.

I THOUGHT THEY'D GET ON WELL. I'LL JUST SLIP OUT NOW BEFORE THEY COME BACK. IN FACT, I THINK THEY'VE ALREADY FORGOTTEN THAT I'M HERE!

But, as usual, she did!

Chris lived up to both girls' expectations. . .

I'VE REALLY ENJOYED TONIGHT, ANN. D'YOU THINK I COULD SEE YOU AGAIN TOMORROW?

OH, YES PLEASE, CHRIS. I'D LIKE THAT.

I'LL HAVE TO GO OUT TOMORROW AND GET SOME NEW CLOTHES. I CAN'T TURN UP FOR THE DATE WEARING ANY OLD RUBBISH. I WON'T SPEND MUCH. . .

I SUPPOSE I DID GO A BIT OVER THE TOP. STILL, I CAN AFFORD TWENTY POUNDS FOR HIGHLIGHTS WHEN THERE'S THREE HUNDRED SAFE AND SOUND IN THE BANK!

But it didn't stop there.

NOW ALL I NEED IS A NEW PAIR OF SHOES...

Back home, Ann soon forgot about the cost...

WELL, WHAT D'YOU THINK?

IT'S NICE, BUT WHY ARE YOU GOING TO ALL THIS TROUBLE? WHO'S YOUR DATE – SIMON LE BON?

NO, CHRIS HARDING.

SUE'S COUSIN! WELL, YOU'LL MAKE A RIGHT PAIR – HE'S ALMOST AS RECKLESS WITH MONEY AS YOU ARE.

FOR A MINUTE THERE I THOUGHT YOU WERE SERIOUS! ANYWAY, I'LL SEE YOU LATER. CHRIS IS PICKING ME UP IN HALF AN HOUR.

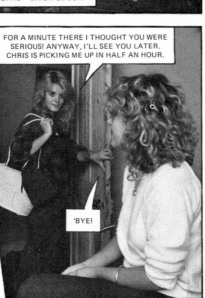

'BYE!

AND WHAT'S THAT SUPPOSED TO MEAN?

WELL, I HEARD HIS BIKE BUSINESS HAD FAILED AND THAT HE WAS BACK IN TOWN. JUST MAKE SURE HE ISN'T AFTER YOUR MONEY!

Despite Chris's protests they ended up going shopping.

LOOK, CHRIS, ISN'T IT NICE?

VERY, BUT WE'LL BE LATE FOR THE FILM IF WE DON'T GO NOW. HAVEN'T YOU BOUGHT ENOUGH FOR ONE DAY?

BUT CHRIS, IT'S SO PRETTY...

LOOK, IF YOU REALLY WANT IT, GET IT NEXT WEEK. NOW LET'S GO!

ONLY SIX POUNDS THIS AFTERNOON...

I MIGHT'VE GUESSED THIS WAS WHY YOU'D BE LATE. WELL, HOW MUCH HAVE YOU SPENT?

YEAH, BUT SIX POUNDS HERE AND THERE DOESN'T ADD UP TO A TICKET FOR PARIS, DOES IT?

I SUPPOSE SHE'S RIGHT. STILL, I'VE GOT OVER TWO HUNDRED POUNDS LEFT. I'LL JUST BE MORE CAREFUL IN FUTURE.

Later.

WE HAD A GREAT TIME, LISA. CHRIS AND I REALLY GET ON WELL.

BUT DID HE PUT UP A FIGHT WHEN YOU PAID FOR HIM TO GO INTO THE CINEMA?

LOOK, I INSISTED, ALL RIGHT? HE'S HAD A LOT OF REPAIRS TO DO ON HIS MOTORBIKE, Y'KNOW.

WELL, I COULD BE WRONG — IT'S JUST A FEELING — BUT IF CHRIS IS A BIT SHORT OF CASH RIGHT NOW, WHAT WITH HIS BUSINESS CLOSING DOWN AND EVERYTHING. . .

. . .I KNOW WHAT YOU'RE TRYING TO SAY, BUT HE HASN'T ASKED ME FOR ONE PENNY. HE'S NOT LIKE THAT, LISA. TAKE MY WORD FOR IT.

Ann tried to put Lisa's doubts out of her mind.

But a couple of days later. . .

HOLD IT, CHRIS, I WANT A WORD.

ER. . .HI, DAVID.

NOW ABOUT THAT TWENTY POUNDS YOU OWE ME, CHRIS. . .

YOU'LL GET IT, DAVID. JUST GIVE ME A FEW MORE DAYS.

LOOK, I'VE GOT TWENTY POUNDS HERE. GO ON, TAKE IT, CHRIS.

He put up a fight, but in the end. . .

THANKS, LOVE, YOU REALLY SAVED MY BACON THERE. AND DON'T WORRY, YOU'LL GET EVERY PENNY BACK. I'VE GOT A BIKE MESSENGER'S JOB LINED UP AND I SHOULD BE ABLE TO START IN A COUPLE OF DAYS

LISA'S WRONG, CHRIS DOESN'T CARE ABOUT MY MONEY. STILL, I WON'T TELL HER I LENT HIM SOME MONEY. SHE WOULDN'T UNDERSTAND.

But the next night.

WHAT'S WRONG, CHRIS? YOU SEEM VERY QUIET FOR SOMEONE WHO'S JUST LANDED A GOOD JOB!

WELL, I CAN ONLY START IF MY MOTOR-BIKE'S WORKING — AND IT NEEDS ANOTHER NEW PART.

IS. . .IS IT MORE MONEY YOU NEED?

YES, LOVE, BUT I OWE YOU A LOT ALREADY. I CAN'T BORROW MORE.

DON'T BE SILLY, HOW MUCH DO YOU WANT?

But after some persuasion.

YOU NEED IT MORE THAN I DO, CHRIS. JUST PAY ME BACK WHEN YOU CAN.

I DON'T KNOW WHAT TO SAY, ANN, BUT WHEN I GET MY FIRST PAY PACKET I'LL BRING IT RIGHT ROUND AND YOU'LL GET EVERY PENNY BACK.

But Ann had been seen.

And when Chris left. . .

YOU CAN'T SAY I DIDN'T WARN YOU! HOW MUCH DID YOU GIVE HIM?

ONLY SIXTY TODAY, BUT LISA. . .

YOU MEAN YOU'VE GIVEN HIM MORE?

Over the last few days Ann had lent Chris quite a lot of money. . .

A FOOL COULD SEE HE'S JUST SPINNING YOU A LINE! GET RID OF HIM, ANN. HE'S NOTHING BUT A SCROUNGER.

CHRIS WOULDN'T DO THAT TO ME – WOULD HE? I'VE GOT TO TALK TO SUE. SHE KNOWS HIM BETTER THAN ANYONE.

So.

OF COURSE LISA'S WRONG! MAYBE HE IS SHORT OF CASH, BUT CHRIS WOULD NEVER DO ANYTHING LIKE THAT!

I KNEW I WAS RIGHT. LOOK, DON'T MENTION THIS TO CHRIS, HE'D BE SO HURT.

OF COURSE I WON'T – YOU CAN TRUST ME.

ER. . .IT'S PROBABLY NOT A GOOD TIME TO MENTION IT, BUT COULD YOU LEND ME A TENNER? I'VE GOT TO GET MUM A BIRTHDAY PRESENT AND. . .

. . .OF COURSE I CAN. DON'T THINK ANOTHER THING ABOUT IT.

But at the weekend, Ann sat down and counted up just how much she was owed. . .

I'VE ONLY GOT THIRTY POUNDS LEFT! STILL, CHRIS SHOULD BE ROUND THIS AFTERNOON. HE GETS PAID TODAY AND SUE SAID SHE'D DROP ROUND WITH THAT TENNER SHE OWES ME.

. . .and realised that for the first time in ages she hadn't spent anything on herself.

But that evening.

I WONDER WHERE CHRIS CAN HAVE GOT TO? HE SAID HE'D BE HERE AT FOUR – AND IT'S GONE FIVE.

WHAT ARE YOU STILL DOING HERE? THOUGHT THE GREAT CHRIS WOULD HAVE ARRIVED WITH HIS CHEQUE BOOK BY N. . .

ER. . .HE MUST'VE HAD TO WORK LATE, OR SOMETHING. . .

SURE! LOOK, ANN, GO ROUND THERE NOW. IF YOU DON'T YOU PROBABLY WON'T SEE YOUR MONEY – OR CHRIS – AGAIN.

So Ann went round to Chris's house. . .

HE IS THERE! AND SUE'S WITH HIM. WHAT — WHAT'S GOING ON?

OH, CHRIS, PLEASE LET HER BE WRONG. . . PLEASE. I COULDN'T BEAR IT IF ALL I EVER MEANT TO YOU WAS HOW MUCH MONEY I COULD GIVE YOU.

e moved r, she d hear t they e saying.

. .AND SHE DID SUSPECT SOMETHING WAS GOING ON, BUT I TALKED HER OUT OF IT.

GOOD, I DID WONDER IF SHE WAS GETTING SUSPICIOUS. . .

I—I CAN'T BE HEARING THIS. PLEASE CHRIS, DON'T DO THIS TO ME!

But as she turned to go.

ANN? WAIT — ANN!

DON'T, CHRIS, PLEASE, NO MORE LIES!

I WAS JUST ON MY WAY ROUND TO SEE YOU. . .

WHY, TO STEAL MORE MONEY FROM ME? HOW COULD YOU, CHRIS? I THOUGHT YOU LOVED ME!

I DO — THAT'S WHY I HAD TO SAVE YOU FROM YOURSELF! LOOK, TWO TICKETS TO PARIS. ONE BOUGHT AND PAID WITH FROM THE MONEY I BORROWED FROM YOU, AND MINE BOUGHT AND PAID FOR WITH MY FIRST WEEK'S WAGES!

YOU MEAN YOU AND SUE. . .

. . .KNOW HOW BAD YOU ARE WITH MONEY AND TOOK THE MATTER INTO OUR OWN HANDS! NOW GO HOME AND PACK YOUR BAGS, WE LEAVE TOMORROW.

TOMORROW? BUT. . .BUT I DON'T HAVE ANYTHING TO WEAR! I'LL HAVE TO GO SHOPPING, AND. . .

Some people never learn their lesson – do they?

THE END

Dear Julie

For several weeks now I've felt that things haven't been right between us. You don't really seem to have noticed — or if you have, you haven't let on.

Anyway, as I said before, things don't seem to be working out between us, and it's time that we both came to realise that.

We've been together for nearly a year now and at first it really was great and we had lots of fun, but I just don't feel the same way about you any more. Don't ask me to explain why this has happened, I can't, but there's no point in carrying on with our relationship if there's no feeling there.

I know I've taken the coward's way out by telling you this in a letter and not to your face, but I knew you'd get into a state and I couldn't face a scene.

Please don't phone me to talk things over, there's nothing more to say.

Adrian

Dear Mark

I know I haven't written for a while but so much has happened recently I just haven't had the chance to keep in touch.

I don't really know where to begin except to say that Julie and I have split up, after exactly nine months, two weeks and three days. Everyone has been shocked by the news, as I'm sure you will be. "But you seemed so happy," people keep saying. And the truth is, we were happy, and very much in love.

Until three weeks ago I'd planned to ask her to marry me on our year long anniversary. I'd even started looking around jewellery shops at diamond engagement rings.

That's a laugh, isn't it? Me, Adrian Richards — getting married! Remember when we were at school? How you and I went everywhere together? We hated girls then, and vowed neither of us would ever get married — we'd live together and go fishing and sailing whenever we wanted!

It doesn't seem all that long ago that we were two runny-nosed little boys, does it?

Now you're at college studying to be a teacher and I'm a fully qualified car mechanic on the point of getting engaged and looking forward to a happy future with Julie — or rather, that was the plan.

Poor Julie, she must have been really shocked when she got my letter telling her it was all over. I couldn't tell her to her face, Mark, I just couldn't.

I can just imagine how her eyes would have filled up with tears as she struggled to ask why, unable to find a reason for my cold and hurtful letter.

I'll never tell her the real reason, although she'll find out for herself eventually. But I'll tell you, Mark, you'll be able to understand why I'm doing things this way.

For three months now I haven't been feeling well — nothing too serious, just a bit dizzy and off-

balance and always very tired. I thought all I needed was a tonic, but when I went to the doctor he didn't prescribe me anything, just gave me a note to see a specialist at the hospital for tests.

I should have realised then that there was something wrong, but I didn't — or maybe I didn't want to. I was unable to face up to reality. But now I have to.

I've never been as happy as I was with Julie and I know that if we'd got married it would have worked. I really love that girl, Mark, more than I ever thought it possible to love anyone. That's why I had to finish with her — it's better for her this way, even though I've caused her a lot of pain and misery.

Like I said, I was sent to the hospital for tests and the results came at the end of last week.

Apparently the disease I've got is in an advanced stage and there's nothing they can do to treat it. They tell me that I've only got six months to live, six months in which to sort everything out. It's not very long, I know, but now I've come to terms with what's going to happen I feel quite positive about what I must do.

Finishing with Julie now means that by the time I die there's a good chance she'll have met someone else and started to forget about how we once felt for each other.

If she knew the truth, I know

she'd stay with me, determined that something could be done to save me. But I know there's no hope and I couldn't bear to see the pain in her eyes as I start to get worse.

I don't need to ask you not to tell anyone, Mark, and I'm sorry you're the one I've burdened with this. But you are my best friend and I did need to tell someone.

Please give me a ring when you get this letter. We've still got so much to talk about.

Adrian

HAVE YOU GOT WHA

Are you right in the know when it comes to looking good? Our quiz will tell you if you've got style — do it if you dare!

1 The boy you've fancied for ages finally gets around to asking you out. He suggests a walk in the park. Do you wear:
a) Your best jeans, with a big cuddly jumper and boots?
b) That smart suit you bought to impress him weeks ago — you've *got* to let him see you in it?
c) Your brother's biggest, baggiest dungarees and wellies?

2 If you were going to your cousin's wedding and you had to wear a hat, would you make it:
a) A chic pull-on trilby?
b) A black job, complete with veil?
c) Your old school beret?

3 For your boyfriend's firm's annual do, would you dress to kill in:
a) A smart dress in dramatic black. Nothing too revealing — you wouldn't want to show him up?
b) A sexy dress in shocking red. Something backless and split to the hip — just to make his workmates drool?
c) Your jeans and a new t-shirt. Why dress up and pretend to be something you're not?

4 For daytime, is your make-up:
a) Light and subtle — pale foundation, peachy blusher, brown or grey eyeshadow and clear lip gloss?
b) Sophisticated — lots of face shaping and highlighting, dramatic black kohl around your eyes and strong lip colour to make the most of your mouth?
c) Non-existent?

5 Your mum and dad ask you to choose a piece of jewellery for your birthday. Would you pick:
a) Something that won't go out of fashion — a slim gold chain or some pearl stud earrings?
b) Something high fashion that you wouldn't be able to afford yourself, like some chunky jet beads?
c) Something high fashion that all your mates will admire — brightly coloured titanium earrings, or a silver-studded wrist band?

6 Meeting his parents for the first time, would you wear:
a) A fairly smart skirt and jumper — something that looks nice, but that you feel comfortable in?
b) A black flying suit with loads of gold jewellery and high-heeled shoes?
c) Your old jeans and a t-shirt with a funny slogan on — something that might give his old mum a laugh?

7 In your opinion, a girl's best friend is her:
a) Clutch bag?
b) Gold ankle chain?
c) Dog?

~~~~~~~~~~~~~~~~~~~~~~~~~~~~~~~~

CONCLUSIONS

Mostly A's. You like to look good all the time, so you tend to stick to the old, tried and trusted formulas. Not for you are the high-fashion looks or revealing dresses — you prefer to look neat and smart. Which you do — all the time. Well done!

Mostly B's. You can look good — but you can also look very Over The Top! You don't believe in neat, smart outfits — you want to be noticed! You love the luxury of good clothes and expensive jewellery. But be careful not to go too far!

Mostly C's. Sorry to say this, but you've really got no idea, have you? Looking good is a bit of a hit-and-miss affair with you — if you do manage to look terrific, it's usually more by accident than design. Take a few tips in taste from *My Guy's* fashion pages in future!

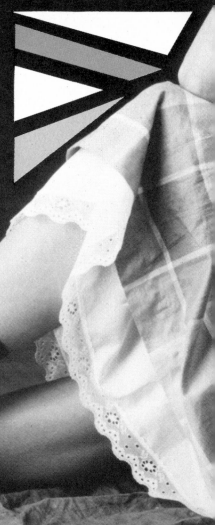

IT TAKES

A DAY IN THE LIFE OF ...BOB!

8.30: The radio springs into action and I spring out of bed to do my exercises. Well, you have to work to keep your body as beautiful as mine.

8.35: Hobble back to bed for a cup of tea. I must have pulled something — and I'm not talking about that blonde Julie saw me with last night . . .

9.00: Wake up with a start. The hot water bottle's leaking — cold water, natch. Breath a sigh of relief — thought I'd had a terrible accident.

9.05: Time for a bowl of bran, nuts and natural yoghurt. You are what you eat . . . that doesn't mean I'm a nut.

9.10: Retire to the bathroom with the newspaper. That bran cereal definitely lives up to its reputation.

9.20: It occurs to me that I'm going to be very late for the office.

9.25: Have another quick cup of tea.

9.30: I get showered, shaved and dressed.

9.45: Leave the house and limp to the bus stop. I definitely have pulled something, that redhead who lives next door is following me . . .

10.15: Arrive at the office. Julie greets me with a sarcastic: ''Good afternoon,'' and I remark about the size of her thighs. It never fails to send her slamming back into her office.

11.15: Finish reading the morning's pile of fan mail. In fact, I finished reading that at 10.20 but then I got involved in an argument with Chris over whose turn it was to buy the tea.

11.25: Chris boots Andy out of the office to get the teabags, I come out from my hiding place under the desk.

11.30: Julie demands to know where the feature is I've been writing for the past three days. Try to fob her off with a mumbled excuse about research. Just as she starts to turn red and clench her fists Andy returns with *coffee* bags and the crisis is averted.

11.45: Sidle out of the office to meet that pretty new brunette in accounts. It's obvious she's impressed by my quick wit and new leather flying jacket. Arrange to meet her for a drink tonight. It gives you such a good feeling when you know you've made someone's day.

12.00: Pop down to McDonald's for a quick Quarter Pounder then back to the office when I'm sure everyone else is out.

12.30: Settle down for forty winks.

2.30: Wake up with Julie standing over me wearing a very dangerous expression. Try to convince her I'm researching for a feature about dreams but it doesn't work.

3.00—5.30: I keep a very low profile. Manage to finish off the crosswords in all the daily papers while Julie swoons over the latest Wham! pin-ups we've had in. Chris, for once, hasn't realised I'm doing nothing because she's busy drooling over Julie's shoulder at those aforementioned pin-ups.

5.35: Shout goodnight and make a run for it.

5.45: Meet my brunette for tonight outside a rather expensive restaurant — horrors! She's reading the menu. Whisk her round the corner to the Chinese pretty smartish.

6.00: Before we've even ordered she's broken down and confessed she's only just split up with her six foot tall, six foot wide, judo black belt, boyfriend. I just hope nothing of mine gets broken if he sees us.

7.00: I try to impress her by eating with chopsticks and accidently flick a king prawn down her blouse. Chaos as I try to get it out and she slaps me round the face.

7.15: Pay the bill and promise the owner that I'll never come back.

7.20: Walk the brunette to the bus stop and leave her quickly. There's a rather large looking fella over the road . . .

7.30: Race home in time for *Coronation Street*.

8.00: Turn over for *Brookside*.

8.30: Work-out to *Lionel Blair Aerobics LP*.

10.00: Fall into bed, a shattered man. Decide that I hate Lionel Blair.

MADNESS
MY GUY

ARE YOU A 'TOM

T'

Are you your boy's best friend? Or do you only have eyes for the guys? Our quiz will tell you!

1. You're in your local club with your fella and his mates. Everyone's glass is empty, so do you:
a) Smile and offer to get the next round in?
b) Smile sweetly and whisper: "Right, whose turn is it to buy me a drink?"
c) Grab your purse and make a mad dash to the ladies until the danger's passed?

2. Do you think pool is:
a) Dead boring to watch?
b) A great game if you happen to be the British champion, like you are?
c) A terrific place to show off your bikini?

3. When out with your mates, does the conversation usually end up with:
a) You falling asleep. You get so *bored* when there are no fellas around?
b) You telling everyone about your latest shark fishing expedition?
c) You moaning about your spots/your figure/your fella, etc.?

4. If your boyfriend calls round unexpectedly, are you usually:
a) Pleased to see him. He can help you with the *Airfix* model you're making?
b) Out?
c) Furious — you don't want him to see you without all your war-paint on?

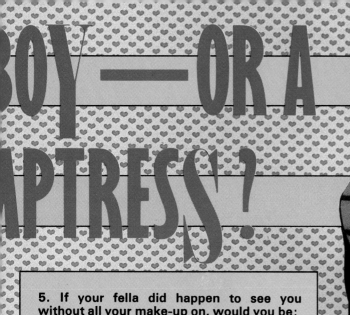

BOY ——OR A MPTRESS?

5. If your fella did happen to see you without all your make-up on, would you be:
a) Not too bothered — you hardly wear any anyway?
b) Extremely ugly?
c) Unrecognisable?

6. Do you think boys make good:
a) Husbands?
b) Friends?
c) Model aircraft?

SCORE

	a	b	c
1	0	10	5
2	5	0	10
3	10	0	5
4	0	5	10
5	0	5	10
6	10	5	0

0-20 — You haven't quite grown out of the stage of playing cowboys and indians with the boy next door, have you? Let's face it, you're still a bit of a tomboy — and that way you're missing out on a lot. Try being a bit more romantic in future. Just because that boy's got his arm round you doesn't mean he wants a spot of arm wrestling, you know . . .

25-40 — You've got the balance just about right. You're not too soppy about boys — in fact, you prefer to treat them as just good friends rather than potential husbands. You don't scare boys off, and the chances are, you're quite a popular girl. Well done!

45-60 — You like to think of yourself as a bit of a *femme fatale* — but the truth is, you just scare boys rigid! Your one aim in life is to attract as many boys as possible — even if someone's heart has to break in the process. Be careful when you play your little love games — because you may end up getting hurt in the end . . .

GET

EVERYONE loves to shop for new clothes. They cheer you up, give you confidence and even put a spring in your step. Unfortunately, they also put a dent in your bank balance, which is why most of us can't afford new clothes as often as we'd like.

But we can afford to keep new clothes looking like new — and give a fresh lease of life to old favourites. Simple carelessness makes even the most expensive things look tacky, while adopting a few good habits can make your clothes last twice as long and look twice as good.

Your clothes say a lot about you. Are yours saying 'scruff' . . ?

CARING FOR YOUR CLOTHES

*No matter how much you may love one particular thing, try not to wear it more than one day at a time. Clothes look fresher if they're given a 'breather' between wears, even when it isn't necessary to clean them.

SMART!

*Never leave your clothes lying around in heaps after wearing them. Hang or fold them properly or they'll soon start to look old and will need constant ironing.

*Shoes with leather soles and heels tend to be slippery, and wear out quicker than plastic ones. Put stick-on soles over the leather ones — the shoes will last twice as long.

*Never put perfume or deodorant directly onto your clothes, as these may stain. Spray them onto *you.*

*Don't hang your clothes up with things still left in the pockets. This will quickly stretch them out of shape.

*If you don't have time to iron something — hang it in a steamy bathroom or over a boiling kettle (keeping a safe distance.) The steam makes creases drop out.

TRICKS OF THE TRADE

A few useful extra tips to make your clothes look really special.

*Most expensive clothes are instantly recognisable by their elegant accessories. Try buying your own special little buttons and replacing the ordinary ones on dresses or blouses. The buttons can be bought cheaply from most department stores, and give your clothes an 'exclusive' look.

*Try storing black clothes inside out — that way they won't collect so much fluff.

If you have a dress that clings to you or your slip when you wear it, try running a wire coat hanger between the dress and slip before you put them on. This cuts down the static that makes them cling.

*When packing a suitcase, always put the heaviest items in first, and try to put bulky things like towels between shoes and more delicate things like blouses.

*Never hang damp clothes on wire hangers — the metal may stain.

STAIN REMOVAL

IT happens to the most careful of us — a spilt drink, a dripping plate — no matter how many precautions you take, you're bound to end up with stains on your clothes sometimes. Here's a guide to help you get rid of some of the most common and awkward stains.

CHEWING GUM: Put the garment in a plastic bag in the freezer, or apply ice cubes until the gum freezes. It should come off easily.

ANTI-PERSPIRANT: Make up a paste using bicarbonate of soda and salt, and apply over the stained area. Then soak and wash, if it's a washable item, or take to the dry-cleaners.

BIRO: Dip the affected spot in a little methylated spirit, soak in a biological washing powder and rinse or dry clean, according to the washing instructions on the label of the garment.

BLOOD: Again — check on the label if the garment can be washed. If it can, soak at once in cold water with lots of salt, or if the stain is old, try soaking overnight in cool water and washing powder. If the item is dry-clean only, then let your cleaner deal with it, but it's important that stains on suede and leather should be gently dabbed with cold water straight away.

GREASE: On washable clothes, scrape off as much of the grease as you can, then dust with talcum powder or cornflour, which should absorb most of the stain. Then wash thoroughly at the highest temperature the garment can stand. If it's a really bad stain, try ironing it between two sheets of white blotting paper with a hot iron.

MASCARA: Rub the garment in undiluted washing-up liquid, then wash as usual. If this doesn't work, try one of the commercial dry-cleaning 'dab-off' solutions. They are widely available, quite cheap, and are very effective on all sorts of awkward stains.

COULD YOU

It takes more than just good looks to make a good model. To be successful, you need self-discipline, a cool head and the ability to look good, even when you don't feel it! Could you make it? Do our quiz and find out if you've got what it really takes. You might be in for a big surprise!

1. Do you spend at least two hours getting made up and dressed to go out anywhere?
Yes/No
2. Do you get impatient at being kept waiting?
Yes/No
3. If you had a rotten cold, would you go straight to bed for a week?
Yes/No
4. Would you mind having to get up early on a Sunday morning to go to work?
Yes/No
5. Do you really envy the models you see in fashion magazines and on television?
Yes/No

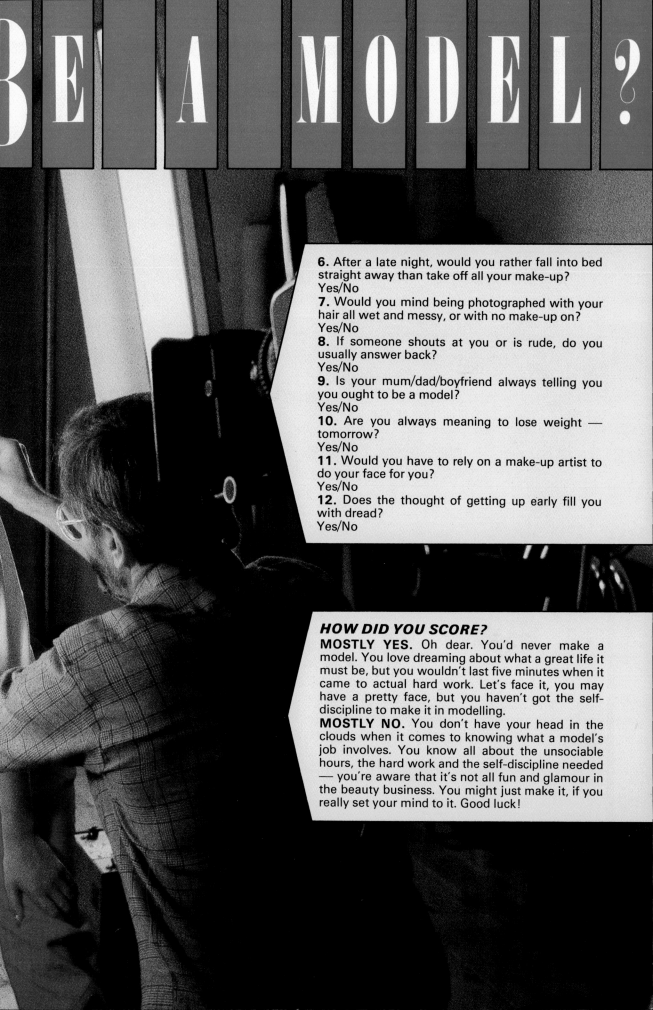

BE A MODEL?

6. After a late night, would you rather fall into bed straight away than take off all your make-up?
Yes/No

7. Would you mind being photographed with your hair all wet and messy, or with no make-up on?
Yes/No

8. If someone shouts at you or is rude, do you usually answer back?
Yes/No

9. Is your mum/dad/boyfriend always telling you you ought to be a model?
Yes/No

10. Are you always meaning to lose weight — tomorrow?
Yes/No

11. Would you have to rely on a make-up artist to do your face for you?
Yes/No

12. Does the thought of getting up early fill you with dread?
Yes/No

HOW DID YOU SCORE?

MOSTLY YES. Oh dear. You'd never make a model. You love dreaming about what a great life it must be, but you wouldn't last five minutes when it came to actual hard work. Let's face it, you may have a pretty face, but you haven't got the self-discipline to make it in modelling.

MOSTLY NO. You don't have your head in the clouds when it comes to knowing what a model's job involves. You know all about the unsociable hours, the hard work and the self-discipline needed — you're aware that it's not all fun and glamour in the beauty business. You might just make it, if you really set your mind to it. Good luck!

BOY?

THERE'S one in every band, and John Keeble is the one in Spandau Ballet — the quiet one, that is! Hidden away behind his drum kit, and quiet in interviews, John seems the shy boy in a band full of extroverts. Or is he . . ?

"I'M a bit of a Jekyll and Hyde really," says John with a grin. "I *can* be quiet — and, of course, I often am. But I can be a raving idiot with the biggest mouth in the band as well!"

John met up with the other members of Spandau at Owens School in Islington, though he didn't really get to know any of them until the fourth year as he was in the year above them. Anyway, he had a great passion in his life at the time which didn't leave him any time for messing about with mere drums — cricket!

"It's quite true," he laughs. "I loved all sports at school, but cricket — well, it was true love!"

After school, John worked for a while at Barclay's Bank as a foreign cashier — an experience which he still groans about!

"I was useless!" he admits happily. "When there were drink-ups after work, when someone left, everyone would sit around in their suits sucking up to the manager while I'd be in my jeans at the bar drinking doubles with the messenger!"

So this shy-boy image isn't entirely accurate then?

"As I said," replies John, "I'm both. When we're on tour, Martin and Steve usually share a room because they're both a bit mad, and I'm in with Gary. Being with Gary makes me all serious and sensible, but if things get out of hand or Steve and Martin plan some prank, I'm the worst of the lot — I'm always the one seen running out of hotels in the middle of the night carrying a chair or something!"

So how does he account for the fact that he's the least well-known of the band?

"Simple," he says cheerfully! "Tony's the singer, so it's natural that he gets lots of attention, then Gary is our mastermind and tends to do all the interviews and stuff. Then Steve and Martin are both pretty good-looking, so . . ."

Such modesty!

"Not really," he says simply. "I'm a realist, but I know my worth, and I'm very ambitious. In fact, I'm very single-minded and I won't let anything — even girls — get in the way of my work."

You see, it's true what they say — still waters can run very deep indeed!

Are You Figh

IS keeping fit a pleasure, a pain or a religion? If you're one of those awful body-bores who can't talk, about anything except new techniques in weight-training — our quiz will reveal the real you!

1. You step on the scales for the first time in months — and you've gained a stone! Do you —
a) Stop eating sweets and fats?
b) Step up your exercise programme?
c) Step off the scales — sharpish?

2. You know you've got to diet, but which diet do you choose?
a) The F-Plan diet — low fat and high fibre?
b) The Beverly Hills diet—all pineapples and papayas?
c) The Ronald McDonald diet?

3. Your new guy is very keen on keep fit, and asks you to come jogging with him. Do you —
a) Agree — you like a good run?
b) Disagree — you need to concentrate to feel the burn, and he'd be a distraction?
c) Put on a pretty pink tracksuit and hop about a bit to keep him happy?

4. ideally, do you think that exercise should —
a) Make you lean and lithe and a better person?
b) Be a carefully-planned programme for life?
c) Be done by other people?

5. What inspired you to take up an exercise class?
a) General concern for your health?
b) Everybody's doing it?
c) The telly broke down?

6. What do you usually wear for your daily work-out?
a) *Fila* tracksuit and *Elis* sweatbands?
b) An old, baggy sweat suit, with an extra jumper when you're warming up?
c) Pink satin shorts and *Slendertone* pads?

7. What kind, and how much exercise do you usually take?
a) A brisk trot from the sofa to the fridge and back, several times a night?
b) A daily work-out to the Jane Fonda LP and a game of tennis at weekends?
c) Jogging every morning, swimming every other day and aerobics twice a week?

8. How would you best describe your physique?
a) Like a new moped — efficient but not very speedy?
b) Like a sports car — fast, well-tuned and decorative?
c) Like an old banger — sluggish and rusty but full of character?

A PHYSICA

	A	B	C
1.	5	10	0
2.	5	10	0
3.	5	10	0
4.	10	5	0
5.	5	10	0
6.	10	5	0
7.	0	5	10
8.	5	10	0

0–35
Lazy, boring, sluggish, probably overweight — but very happy!

You've managed to escape the trap of taking up sport as a fashion fad, but now you've proved your point, you could try just, well — *walking* a bit would be a start!

35–65
You're aware of health matters without being a fanatic. You realise that exercise and a sensible diet are important, and enjoy being physical for the sake of being physical — not for the sake of a trend and having something to talk about.

65–80
Yes, you're probably fighting fit, but you also epitomise the physical jerks. You've adopted the new craze with all its jargon and status symbols and got caught up in a simple craze. Your body may be perfect — congratulations. But what about your brain . . ?

ing Fit

OR

JeRk?

CRACKING LOVE COD

I really fancy this boy at our local youth club. I think he likes me too because he's always staring at me. I told my mate I liked him and she asked him out for me, but he said 'no'.

What should I do?

This girl has just made two of the most classic mistakes. One, instead of talking to the boy herself, she's gossiped to her friend about him. And two, she's got her mate to ask him out for her.

These are both really bad mistakes, because she's probably embarrassed him no end. And if that's happened, it's unlikely he'll ever get round to asking her out as she wants.

The only way to find out if a boy really likes you is to approach him yourself. If he does like you, you shouldn't have too much of a problem getting into conversation. Then you can find out for yourself whether he's worth getting to know or not, instead of relying on what your friend says.

Of course, there is always the added problem that the guy and your friend will hit it off, and he may ask her out instead of you! So get in there first!

Don't feel afraid of asking him out yourself if he seems shy. No-one's asking you to march straight up to the boy you fancy and say, "Will you come to the pictures with me on Saturday?" but once you get into conversation and the chance arises, there's no reason why you shouldn't suggest getting together on your own one day. It doesn't have to sound like a proper date. An invitation round to your place to listen to your new Culture Club album won't

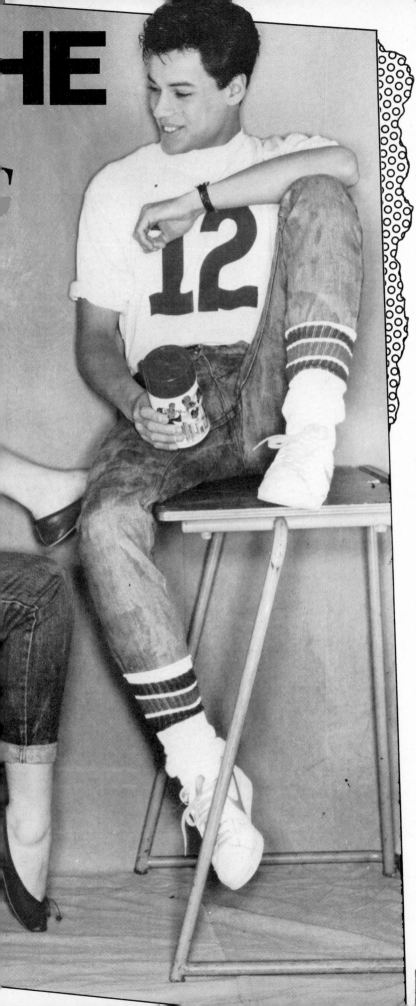

HE

leave either of you feeling embarrassed — and he might just say 'yes'! Go on, why not give it a try?

I thought I was really lucky when I started going out with Wayne because all my mates fancied him like mad. But we've been going out together for six months now, and I'm starting to get a bit bored. All Wayne ever talks about is motor bikes, football, his latest stereo and other things I'm not interested in. It's really getting me down.

This girl's just committed another classic mistake — falling for a pretty face rather than someone whose interests are the same as hers.

Admit it, you've probably done it yourself once or twice — gone out with a boy because all your friends fancied him like crazy and you thought it would be good to be seen around with him, then found out he was dead boring!

Remember, when it comes to going out with someone, it's really their personality that counts rather than their looks. Wouldn't you rather go out with someone who was shorter/spottier/younger than you, but who shared your mad passion for McDonalds' hamburgers, than for someone who was really good-looking but who never said a word? It's worth thinking about, next time you're on the lookout for a new fella.

I keep hinting to my boyfriend that I want to finish with him, but he just can't seem to accept it. I've tried flirting with other boys when I'm out on a date with him and being 'out' when he rings me, but he just keeps on ringing anyway.

I'd like to go out with other boys. How can I get rid of him without hurting his feelings and causing a big upset?

Saying goodbye is always really difficult — especially if you're the one doing the leaving. But if you really don't want to hurt your boyfriend's feelings, the best way is to tell him straight that it's over. Okay, he'll probably be shocked and upset at first, but it's a lot easier to get over than months of two-timing, hinting and generally being nasty.

The longer you leave it, the more painful it will be, for the both of you. He will feel rejected and lack confidence and you will feel guilty because of your unreasonable behaviour.

Many girls believe that the only way to get rid of a boy is by behaving so badly that in the end *he* has to drop *them*. But this is a silly, immature attitude.

If you want to say goodbye, then say it. Don't get anyone to do your dirty work for you.

A girl's

Rupert was Judy's best friend, someone she could trust and love. She'd be lost without him . . .

RUPERT, I shall call him Rupert, I decided, scooping the little puppy up into my arms and kissing him on the head.

"Are you sure that's the one you want?" Dad asked, frowning at the scruffy little bundle in my arms. "It's only a mongrel, you know."

"I know he is," I smiled. "And I'm certain — this is the one I want."

"Well, it's your birthday present," he shrugged. "It's up to you."

Rupert wriggled in my arms and licked me with his little, pink tongue.

"I'll go and pay for him and buy him some food," Dad smiled. "And I'd better get him a lead!"

The pet shop was crowded but I wasn't interested in any of the other animals, now that I had my very own Rupert.

EXCUSES

I'd wanted a dog for as long as I could remember but there'd always been some reason why I couldn't have one. Now I was old enough to look after him myself, though, Mum and Dad had finally run out of excuses.

"Couldn't you have got one with a pedigree?" Mum asked when we got home and I proudly held Rupert out to her. "He's not exactly nice to look at."

"I think he's gorgeous," I defended him. "And so what if he has got funny markings and one ear that sticks up? I think it makes him look distinguished."

"Well, I hope he doesn't make too much mess," she sighed. "We've only just had the living room carpet cleaned." And off she stomped into the kitchen

It was typical of Mum to worry about the house, that was all she really cared about. And I knew that was why she wasn't keen on me having a dog. But Rupert was so adorable and I knew he'd win her over in the end.

Time seemed to fly with him to keep me company. Instead of coming home from school and moping around in my room, I'd spend ages playing silly games with him or brushing his coat till it shone.

I knew I'd never feel lonely again now I had Rupert at my side.

When he was old enough I started taking him for walks, and I was at my happiest wandering through the park watching him running after leaves, or chasing his tail.

SPECIAL

At last I had my own special friend, someone I could tell all my secret hopes and fears to. I knew the girls at school would think I was daft if they knew how I talked to Rupert. But it was all right for them, they weren't as painfully shy as I was and they had loads of friends that they could confide in.

But one day when I got home Rupert wasn't at the gate to meet me. Straight away I knew something was wrong.

"Mum — Mum," I shouted, running into the house. "Where's Rupert?"

"He got out through the garden gate," she said, coming out from the kitchen. "I called and called, but he didn't come back."

Tears streamed down my face. I couldn't believe what she was telling me. It was like a nightmare.

"I hate you! I hate you!" I sobbed. "You've never liked Rupert, you don't care that he could have been knocked down, all you care about is keeping your rotten house tidy!"

Before she could say a word, I turned and ran out into the busy street, calling Rupert's name over and over again, until I was hoarse.

I must have walked miles and miles looking for him and it was dark before I finally gave in and went back home.

Dad was waiting for me, a worried look on his face.

"Mum told me what happened," he said softly. "You know you shouldn't have spoken to her like that, Judy."

"I know," I whispered. "But I was so upset . . ."

"I've contacted the Police," he went on. "And they said they'd let us know if he was handed in. And I've drawn up a notice to stick on the tree in the front garden, asking if anyone's seen him."

"Thanks," I murmured, trying to hold back another gush of tears. "I've just got to get him back, Dad."

But despite all our efforts the weeks dragged slowly by and there was still no sign of little Rupert. I tortured myself with visions of him being knocked over by a car and most nights I cried myself to sleep.

But then one day I saw him.

I'd gone to the shops to get some tea for Mum and just as I was passing the big housing estate nearby I saw him, being carried into a house by a gang of small children.

FOUND

"Rupert," I gasped, hardly able to believe my eyes. And then I was running across the street to the shabby looking house and its overgrown garden.

The children had disappeared inside, and when I rang the bell a tired-looking young woman opened the door.

"Er-hello," I stuttered, not sure what to say. "I'm sorry to disturb you, but I've just seen some children bring my dog in here. He got out of our garden three weeks ago and I've been looking for him ever since."

"Oh dear," she sighed, running a hand through her untidy hair.

Best Friend

"You'd better come in."

Stepping over cluttered boxes of toys and games she led me through into the kitchen.

Outside in the garden I could see Rupert racing up and down after a ball. I had to admit he looked very healthy and he was obviously enjoying himself.

"My little boy found him sitting at the end of the road," she explained. "He didn't have a collar on or anything so we had no way of finding his owner. Anyway, the kids have always wanted a dog and if I could have afforded one, I'd have let them have one ages ago. So when Robert brought Scamp home I let him keep him.

"Rupert," I gulped. "His name's Rupert."

She smiled weakly. "I suppose you'll be wanting him back."

SILENCE

An uneasy silence fell between us as I looked around the tatty house and back at Rupert.

He seemed so happy, so at home in that overgrown garden. At our house he wasn't allowed in the dining room or the bedrooms and if he went in the garden, he had to be watched in case he did any damage.

In fact, the only fun he had was when I came home from school and took him out. I'm sure he could sense Mum didn't like him.

"Think of Rupert," I told myself. "It's what's best for him that matters."

"I'll go and get him for you," the woman said, going to the back door.

"No — no," I said quickly. "It's all right. I think he'd be better off with you. I'm out all day, so he doesn't get that much attention. He'll be better off here with the children."

"Are you sure?" she gasped. "That's really kind of you."

"Of course," I said brightly, trying to hide the tremble in my voice. "I expect my Dad'll buy me another one anyway."

But walking home, I knew I wouldn't get another dog. Rupert was my special friend and no-one could replace him.

And sometimes when I'm alone in my room at night I cry for the feel of his cold, wet nose on my face as he licked me or the smell of his fur when I cuddled him — and for the only real friend I ever had — and lost.

HAVE YOU GOT
TEMPT

TEMPTATION sneaks up on all of us, but do you give in to it — or resist? Read on and discover how to cope and how *you* cope when faced with those terribly tempting situations . . .

TYPES OF TEMPTATION			
*	**	***	****
MILD TEMPTATION	MINOR TEMPTATION	SERIOUS TEMPTATION	TERRIBLE TEMPTATION

FOOD

* * RESIST THE TEMPTATION to eat when you're not really hungry. Make a phone call, wash your hair — anything rather than raid the fridge.

* * RESIST THE TEMPTATION to eat in front of someone who's dieting. It'll improve both your figures.

* RESIST THE TEMPTATION to go on a starvation diet. You may lose weight quickly, but one binge will put it all back on.

* * RESIST THE TEMPTATION to reach for that ultra-fattening cream cake. If you're *really* hungry, a piece of fruit will get rid of the pangs.

* * * RESIST THE TEMPTATION to cheat on your diet. The only person who'll lose by it is you — and we don't mean pounds!

MONEY

* * * **DON'T** spend money you don't really have to impress your mate, fella or folks.

* * **DON'T** borrow money you know you can't pay back!

* **DON'T** lend money to someone who you know *can't* pay *you* back!

* * * **DON'T** blow all your cash on one item. You never know what emergencies might crop up in the future.

* * * **DON'T** buy on impulse. But if you still want the same thing a week later, and can afford it, go and get it.

FRIENDS

* * * **NEVER** gossip about your mates. If you gossip, it follows that other people do, too, even if sworn to secrecy — and whatever you said will soon get back to your mate.

* * * **NEVER** use her as an alibi. If you're caught out, you'll *both* be in hot water — and she won't thank you for that.

A TASTE FOR ATION?

* * YOU SHOULDN'T play hard to get. Guys don't like playing games.

* * * YOU SHOULDN'T see other guys behind his back. You could lose him — and your good reputation.

* * * YOU SHOULDN'T expect him to pay on all your dates. If you do, he'll soon find someone else who's not such a miser.

* * * NEVER make her feel left out. If she's without a fella, try to include her in your plans and convince her she won't be a gooseberry.

* * NEVER tell her that her hair or new dress looks awful. She could mistake your honesty for bitchiness.

* NEVER try to keep up with, or copy, her. She might feel flattered at first, but that'll soon wear off . . .

FELLAS

* * YOU SHOULDN'T nag your fella. Use gentle persuasion to get your own way.

* * YOU SHOULDN'T compare him to other guys. It won't be long before he turns round and tells you to find *another* guy if you do!

FASHION

* * STOP YOURSELF buying something fashionable if it doesn't really suit you. Take your mum, or a mate, along for some objective advice.

* * * STOP YOURSELF buying something you don't really need. Just think what else you could buy with the money.

* * STOP YOURSELF buying something a size too small — hoping that you'll slim into it. (You know you probably won't!)

* STOP YOURSELF shopping at all the 'in' places. You'll get exactly what you're looking for elsewhere — and it'll probably be a lot cheaper.

* * STOP YOURSELF if you see something you like, but know that your best mate's already got it. Think how embarrassing it'll be if you both turn up somewhere wearing identical outfits.

The BUMPER

Every week I answer your body problems in *My Guy* and over the past months I've noticed that there are some things that bother you more than others. I've decided to answer those here. Remember, any time you've got a problem, I'll do my best to help you.

PREGNANT-AND ON THE PILL?

Is it possible to get pregnant while you're on the Pill?

The reason I'm asking is that I'm eighteen and on the Pill, but I've missed a period and my breasts feel very large and sore.

Do you think I could be pregnant?

Maria, Gloucester.

It's unlikely that you could get pregnant while you're on the Pill, but it is possible.

For example, if a girl doesn't take it regularly, or is on certain antibiotics, or has diarrhoea, then there is a slim chance of her getting pregnant.

But lots of things can delay a period, worry or shock for example, so there's no need for you to get too worked up about this.

Make an appointment to see your doctor and have a pregnancy test. That way you'll know for certain whether you're pregnant or not.

TROUBLE DOWN BELOW

I've got a very unpleasant discharge and my vagina is itchy and sore.

Why is this?

Debra, Birmingham.

It sounds to me as if you've got Thrush, which is a fungal infection that thrives in an acid environment, making teenage girls quite likely to suffer from it.

You see, during puberty there are quite heavy acid secretions in the vagina, making these infections likely.

I'm sorry to say it won't clear up on its own, you must see your doctor for an effective treatment.

In the meantime, keep yourself scrupulously clean, change your underwear every day and wear only cotton pants.

MY NAILS ARE A STATE

My boyfriend and I are planning to get engaged, but he says he won't buy me a ring until I've grown my nails.

How can I stop myself biting my fingernails ? I've been doing it for years.

Wendy, Bude.

All it boils down to is will-power and if you want that ring badly enough, then you'll stop chewing your nails, won't you?

It won't be easy breaking a habit like this, but you could try painting your nails with one of those nasty tasting potions you can buy, or use a pretty-coloured varnish, so that you start to take a pride in them.

AM I GOING BLIND

I'm really frightened that I might be going blind. You see, the other night I was watching a programme on the television and my vision went blurred. It's happened since then as well.

What's wrong with me? Am I going blind?

Carol, Cardiff.

It sounds to me as though you've been neglecting your eyes and overstrained them. Perhaps you've been studying too hard, or reading by bad light.

BODY PAGE

Whatever the reason, you need to see an optician and have your eyes tested.

It's possible you'll need to wear glasses and if so, the optician will be able to tell you how to go about getting them.

Make an appointment today, before your eyes get any worse.

PERIODS ARE A PAIN

Every month I suffer agonies with period pains. Sometimes they're so bad I have to go to bed.

What can I do to make coming on more bearable?

Tracey, London.

When your period pains next start, put a hot-water bottle on the small of your back or directly on your stomach. If you feel it is necessary, take a painkiller, such as *Paracetamol.*

There are certain things you can do before your period which might help, such as eating a bran cereal for breakfast to ensure you don't get constipated and taking as much exercise as possible.

However, if none of these measures makes any difference, then you ought to see your doctor.

He'll be able to prescribe you some tablets that will help.

I LOOK LIKE A MAN!

My problem is terrible. You see, I'm covered in hair! It's all over my back, down my chest and as for my arms and legs — well, I look like a man.

Please give me some advice, I'm absolutely desperate.

Louise, Lancs.

Everyone has body hair, it's just that some of us have more than others, or what we've got shows more as in the case of dark haired people.

However, if the hair you talk about is really thick and not like the fine downy hairs most people have, then I think you ought to see your doctor and have a check-up.

It may be that you've got a hormone imbalance and he'll be able to prescribe you some tablets to put that right.

WILL MASTURBATION HARM ME?

I've been masturbating for almost a year now and although I've tried, I just can't stop.

What's really bothering me is that I might be doing myself some bodily harm by doing this.

Could I?

Penny, Hull.

No, physically you can't do yourself any harm. Most people masturbate at some point in their lives, usually during adolescence when there is an awakening of sexual feelings and responses.

So don't worry or feel guilty about what you're doing, it is perfectly normal and harmless.

WHY DOES MY NOSE BLEED?

Over the past few months I've had a lot of nose bleeds. Some of them have been quite heavy.

Why is this happening?

Annie, Brighton.

Nose bleeds are caused by a tiny blood vessel in the nose bursting. Often no reason can be found for a nose bleed, though, and lots of things can trigger one off.

Light nose bleeds are nothing to worry about, but when you start to lose a lot of blood then there's a chance of you becoming anaemic and you ought to see your doctor to prevent that from happening.

I CAN'T USE TAMPONS!

I've tried using tampons on several occasions, without any success. There seems to be something blocking the way.

What is this?

Sue, Carlisle.

Covering the entrance to the vagina is a thin membrane, or skin, called the hymen. It has a hole in it and the size of this varies from girl to girl.

Some girls find using tampons very easy, but others, like yourself, find it quite painful or even impossible.

So, the first thing you've got to do is try and relax. Have a nice warm bath and then try using a tampon. If you find that it still hurts, then stop and try again a few months later.

There's no hurry, is there?

IF YOU'VE

I'm always here to help you. You can write to me at this address: My Guy, 21st Floor, King's Reach Tower, Stamford Street, London SE1 9LS.
In the meantime, here are a selection of letters from my postbag . . .

Am I Too Old?

I've been going out with my boyfriend Des for two months now, and we get on really well. Our only problem is that Des is a year and a half younger than me.

I don't mind because Des is very mature for his age. But all my mates keep going on about it, calling him a baby, and me a cradle-snatcher. It's really getting me down.

It's got so bad I'm thinking of ditching Des, just to shut them up.

Do you think that I'm really too old for him?

Julie, Newcastle.

No, I don't think you're too old for him. And I certainly don't think you should prove your nasty mates right by breaking up the relationship.

If you and Des get on well together, then that's all that matters. Besides, in a year or so, this 'huge' age gap won't be so important anyway.

So ignore your friends, and carry on being happy with Des. They'll soon stop teasing when the novelty wears off.

HE WON'T SPEAK TO ME

There's a boy I really like down at our local youth club. He knows I fancy him, but he won't make an effort to speak to me.

All my mates know how I feel about him, and they're always teasing us about it. But whenever they start, he just walks off or gives me a dirty look.

How can I get to know him better? I spend nearly all my time watching him and thinking about him. Sometimes I cry myself to sleep at night because I think I might never get the chance to go out with him.

Depressed, Manchester.

You're not exactly playing hard to get, are you?

Put yourself in his place for a moment. How would you feel if some boy kept following you around, staring at you and telling everyone how much he loved you? You'd think he was a right pain in the neck, wouldn't you?

But how would you feel if the same boy didn't do all these things, but was generally a good laugh, nice to know and fun to have around? You'd probably be fascinated by him and go all out to get to know him, wouldn't you?

So that's how you've got to behave with this lad. Start acting a bit cool — don't chase after him with your heart on your sleeve.

It's the only way that you're going to get him interested in you, believe me.

And you could also try keeping your feelings for this boy to yourself for a change.

Those teasing mates of yours are probably scaring this boy off!

I'M SO JEALOUS

Please help me with my problem. I've been going out with Gary for nearly a year now, and we love each other very much. But my problem is, I'm really jealous of other girls.

I get really upset and suspicious on the nights I don't see him, even though I know he's at home, or just out with his mates. And if he so much as glances at another girl, I go completely mad, accusing him of all kinds of things.

I know I'm being unreasonable, but how can I stop?

Lynn, Ayrshire.

By reminding yourself how pathetic you're being, and how much you're putting your relationship with this boy at risk by behaving in this unreasonable way.

He sounds a nice, understanding lad. But if you carry on like this, it won't be long before he starts getting fed-up with your behaviour — or worse, living up to the very reputation you're giving him.

You behave like this because you're terrified of losing him. But what you've got to realise is that by behaving in this insecure way, you're doing more to scare him off than to keep him.

So relax, stop worrying — and learn to enjoy your relationship, instead of fearing it.

SHOULD I TAKE HIM BACK?

I went out with Barry for about four months. But then he started beating me up whenever we had a big argument, so I decided to break up with him.

That was six months ago. Lately, he's started coming round again, and I realise I still care about him very much.

He reckons he's changed and that he's got his violent streak under control. He wants me to go out with him again, but I don't know what to do. What do you advise?

Sarah, Cleethorpes.

No matter how much you care

GOT PROBLEMS

about him, or how much you miss him I wouldn't advise you to go back to Barry.

Okay, he might make all the promises in the world that he's a reformed character. But deep down there'll always be the feeling that if he's hit you before, he can do it again.

So if I were you, I'd try to stay friends with Barry — but give your love to someone else, someone you know you can trust.

I CAN'T MAKE FRIENDS

I've just started at a new school in the third year and my problem is, no matter how hard I try, I just can't seem to make friends with anybody.

All the other girls in my class seem to have teamed up with a best friend, but no girl wants to be my best friend. I never get invited round to other people's houses, like the other girls. I seem to spend all my time sitting alone in my bedroom.

Why doesn't anyone want me?
Tiffany, Streatham.
I'm sure it isn't unfriendliness that's stopping these girls getting to know you, Tiffany. It might just be natural shyness.

And just because every girl seems to have a best friend, that doesn't mean they can't have other, not quite so best friends, too. People aren't just restricted to one mate each, you know!

My advice is to try again with these girls. Go up to them and start talking.

If you're feeling shy, you can ask them something about school, then get on to subjects like who their favourite band is, etc.

And just because you're not getting invited round to their houses every night, that's no reason why you can't ask them round to *yours*, is it?

Don't be afraid. Make a start today. You won't be sitting alone in your bedroom for much longer — honest!

MUM WON'T LET ME OUT!

I'm sixteen and my problem is my mum won't let me stay out late. All my mates can stay out as late as they like, but my mum insists I've got to be in the house by ten every night — and she won't let me out at all for three nights a

week, because she says I've got to study hard for my 'O' levels.

I reckon she's just being rotten because she never goes out anywhere herself.

It's got to the point where I can't wait to leave home and do things my way.

Do you think I'm right?
Sharon, Swindon.
You're going to hate me for saying this, Sharon — but no, I don't think you're right!

Your mum's not being unfair, making you stay in a couple of nights a week to study for your exams. I'm sure she's aware of how important your qualifications are — and I reckon you'll thank her for it in

the end when you get good results.

As for not letting you stay out later than ten, I suppose she's just anxious about you wandering the streets on your own late at night and perhaps getting attacked. It's a very natural reaction.

The only way round this one is to prove to her that you *will* be safe, and that you can be trusted to look after yourself.

When you're going out, arrange to come home with a friend, or better still, ask to stay overnight at a friend's house.

If your mum's sure you're not alone and that you're safe, I'm sure she'll be more understanding about your coming-home time.

Guys — I'll Help You Too!

She Won't Pay!

I'm on the dole but my girlfriend has got a good job and earns quite a bit of money.

I really like her, but the only trouble is, she refuses to pay for herself on dates.

I don't expect her to pay for me, but when I suggested she might fork out for herself, she got quite shocked and accused me of not loving her.

I *do* love her. Should I give in and go on paying for her out of my dole money?

Ian, Glasgow.
She may rant and rave about *you* not loving *her*. But I don't think her attitude is exactly loving, either! She's being extremely selfish and inconsiderate, and she's taking you for a ride.

Loving is about sharing, not being paid for every time you go out. She's being very unreasonable if she expects you to make your tiny amount of dole money stretch to cover two of you, while she keeps all her cash for herself.

Tell her that from me. And if she still expects you to pay for her, then I'd advise you to start looking for someone else. Someone who does care about you enough to share your problems.

Answers to Anonymous

Worried, Selkirk. Yes, you're right — you *can* get pregnant in the way you describe. You took a very silly risk and I sincerely hope you've learned your lesson. Don't ever do it again — you might not be so lucky next time.
Jane, Crawley. This boy is just using you, and you know it. He's broken too many girls' hearts to be serious about

what he says this time, so don't believe his empty promises.
Linda, Bromley. You're worrying too much over nothing. I'm sure your boyfriend didn't mean what he said about that girl. I think it's highly unlikely he'd go off with her, not if you're meant to be engaged. If I were you, I'd tell him about your fears and let

him put your mind at rest.
June, Exeter. Your doctor is the only person who can help. This is very common and can be easily treated.
Ashamed, Ilford. Tell your parents what you've done. I'm sure they'll be more supportive than you imagine and will stand by you if necessary, but you must prove you can be honest with them now.

We knew you'd all be really fascinated to find out, so we pinned Trevor down and asked him to pen us a few words about his plans for the New Year. Wish we hadn't asked now . . .

A year in the life of *Trevor*

January

Will probably end the New Year festivities with a big bash Chez Trevor. Not too big, you understand. Probably just yours truly, a few of the Spands, Georgie and little Andy, Simon and Clare (if it's not the chauffeur's night off, natch), and maybe my mum and old Malcolm, if he promises to behave himself and doesn't let his gerbil loose among the fishpaste sandwiches like he did last year. Oh, and I might pop up to Brum to help old John "the quiff" Taylor paint his ceiling — got to keep promises.

Apart from that, bit of a quiet start, really.

February

Spring cleaning starts in earnest Chez Trev. Will make mental note to keep close eye on one's mother, who last year inadvertently threw out entire matchbox collection, along with draft of first novel, *Trev Pulls It Off*. Around mid-Feb, will perhaps consider sending Valentine to Lorraine. Handmade, of course — if aged mother doesn't decide to throw out entire felt pen collection, too.

March

Should see the launch of my new book, *Famous Trevors In History*. The publicity boys over at the publishers are raving about it. "A triumph", they're saying, "Blows the cover right off the whole Trevor story". Hope I manage to finish it.

Have *you* ever realised just how few of the world's geniuses are actually called Trevor? Present company excepted, of course.

April

April Fool's Day. Will make determined effort to avoid pathetic brother's attempts to rattle one, by leaping out of knife drawers clutching rubber hatchets, presenting one with squirting bunches of flowers and ridiculous messages to "ring Mr C. Lion at London Zoo".

He must think I'm as stupid as he is.

May

Back into the recording studio. Not to help out Tone (Hadley) and the boys with their latest effort this time, but to put the finishing touches to my latest LP, *Shape Up and Trim with Trevor*. Well, I reckoned if Angela Rippon and Lionel 'Flares' Blair could do it for the mums, why couldn't I help all my hip friends fight the flab?

I was a bit nervous about doing it at first, mind — being a modest type and all that — but the big boys at EMI were determined. "We need someone with the body of Sylvester Stallone, and the charisma of Simon Le Bon," they cried. "We need someone with the muscles of John Travolta and the voice of Tony Hadley!"

But they couldn't find anyone to fit the bill, so I offered to do it instead.

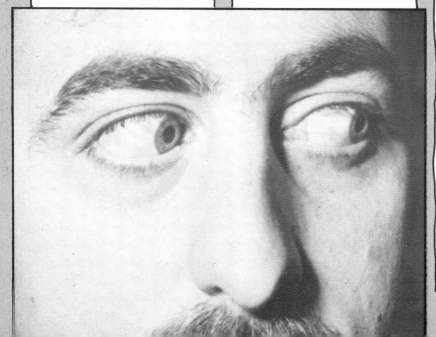